SARDINIAN BRIGADE

GREAT NOVELS AND MEMOIRS OF WORLD WAR I

1. THE MEMOIRS OF GEORGE SHERSTON *by* Siegfried Sassoon
   (Incorporating MEMOIRS OF A FOX-HUNTING MAN, MEMOIRS
   OF AN INFANTRY OFFICER *and* SHERSTON'S PROGRESS)

2. SAGITTARIUS RISING *by* Cecil Lewis

3. SARDINIAN BRIGADE *by* Emilio Lussu

EMILIO LUSSU

Sardinian Brigade

A Giniger Book

published in association with

STACKPOLE BOOKS

TRANSLATED FROM THE ITALIAN BY

MARION RAWSON

J'ai plus de souvenirs
que si j'avais mille ans.

BAUDELAIRE

NOTE

EMILIO LUSSU, a native of Sardinia, fought during the whole of the
war with the Sardinian "Sassari brigade," the most famous infantry brigade in the Italian army. The Sar-
dinians have always been noted for
their bravery, and throughout the war
the Sassari brigade was continually
called upon to take part in the most
serious of the fighting. Lussu, who
twice received special promotion for
services in the field, was also awarded
two bronze medals for military valour,
two silver medals for military valour,
one *"croce di cavaliere"* of the Order
of the Corona d'Italia, one *"croce di
guerra,"* and one *"citation à l'ordre de
l'armée française."* He was once very
seriously wounded. It would seem
well to mention this particularly distinguished record since no reference to
it occurs in the following book. This,
however, will cause no surprise to those
already familiar with Emilio Lussu's
remarkable subsequent career.

Preface

THE READER WILL FIND NEITHER ROMANCE NOR HIS-
tory in this book. It consists simply of personal memories, put together in somewhat haphazard fashion
and limited to one year only, out of the four during
which I served on the Italian front. I have recounted
nothing but what I saw and what made the deepest
impression on me, drawing, not upon my imagina-
tion, but simply on my memory. My comrades in
arms will easily recognize both the incidents I have
described and those who figure in the narrative, despite some altered names. I have not allowed my subsequent experiences to influence my attitude, but
have described the war as it actually was to us then,
with all that we believed and felt at the time. It is not
a work written round a theme; it has been written
simply with the intention of providing an Italian ac-

count of the Great War. In Italy no such books about the war exist as those that have been published in England, France, and Germany. And even this one would never have been written had I not been compelled to spend a period of enforced inactivity.

EMILIO LUSSU

Clavadel-Davos
April 1937

SARDINIAN BRIGADE

Chapter 1

AT THE END OF MAY 1916 MY BRIGADE, CONSISTING OF the 399th and 400th regiments, was on the Carso. We had been fighting on this front ever since the beginning of the war, and we were heartily sick of it. Every inch of ground reminded us of some engagement or of the grave of a fallen comrade. Over and over again we had captured trenches from the enemy, but the situation remained just the same. There were always more to be taken. Trieste seemed still as far away as ever, lying as though weary in the summer heat, between us and the sea. Our artillery had not as yet fired a single shot. The Duke of Aosta, who was in command of our army corps, mentioned it every now and then in dispatches or in his speeches, by way of giving us some encouragement.

The Duke had little military ability, but considerable literary enthusiasm. He and his Chief of Staff complemented each other: one wrote the speeches and the other delivered them. Having learned them by heart, the Duke recited them in the oratorical manner of an ancient Roman, with impeccable diction. Every important ceremony (and they were frequent enough) was crowned by one of these orations. Unfortunately, the Chief of Staff possessed no great talent for composition. So that in the end the army remembered the speeches for the Duke's delivery of them rather than for what they contained. He had a fine voice, too. But otherwise he was pretty unpopular.

One afternoon news reached us that the Duke had ordered our withdrawal from the front line for some months' rest, as a reward for all that our brigade had been through. As the news was soon followed by orders to prepare to be relieved by another brigade, it was obviously true. The men were jubilant, and cheered the Duke. At long last it appeared that there was some advantage in having a prince of the royal house as army corps commander. No one else could have granted us so long a spell away from the front. Until then our only respite from the trenches had been for short periods spent a few miles to the rear, and within range of the enemy artillery. On this occasion rumour even went so far as to suggest—and the report spread like lightning—that the Duke intended us to be quartered in some town. For the first time since the beginning of the war he became quite popular, and it was even asserted and fully believed that he had had a serious difference of opinion on the ques-

tion with General Cadorna and had taken up the
cudgels on our behalf.

Our brigade was duly relieved, and the same night
we went down into the plain. We were to go into
billets at Aiello, a little town near the former frontier
between Italy and Austria.

Our joy was unbounded. At last life was worth living! Our minds were full of plans for the future.
Perhaps after Aiello we might even get to some big
town. Udine, for instance.

After two days' march we reached Aiello. We entered it in the morning, my battalion (the 3rd) leading, with the 12th company at its head. I remember
our entrance well.

The 12th company was commanded by a cavalry
officer, Lieutenant Grisoni. He had been orderly officer to the general in command of our brigade. When
the latter died as the result of a wound, Grisoni asked
to remain with the brigade, and he was now serving
with my battalion. Ordinarily it would have been impossible for a cavalry officer to be assigned to an infantry regiment; but the general in command of the cavalry had made a special exception in his case and had
given him permission to keep his cavalry rank and his
horse. He was a well-known figure in the brigade.
On August 21, 1915 he had led a surprise attack, with
forty volunteers, on a strongly defended advance
trench held by a whole battalion of Hungarians and
had captured it. The exploit was one of exceptional

daring. But he had become famous for another. One evening when we were in a rest camp down the line, Grisoni, after drinking rather too much Piedmontese wine, had ridden his horse into the officers' mess, where the colonel and his regimental staff were dining. He had not uttered a word, but the horse had made straight for the colonel, and pranced and neighed round his chair for some minutes. As a result Grisoni narrowly escaped being sent back to his own regiment.

The battalion marched into the main square of the town, where the general in command of the brigade, together with our regimental commander and the civil authorities of the town, were awaiting us.

The leading company was marching four abreast. The men were covered with mud from the trenches, but this only added to their martial air and made the parade the more impressive. As he came level with the place where the important personages were standing, Lieutenant Grisoni stood up in his stirrups and shouted: "Eyes left!"

This was the salute for the general. It was also a signal for which the 1st platoon had been waiting. Immediately a carefully prepared fanfare pealed forth. A trumpet made out of a large tin coffee-pot blared out the order to march at attention, whereupon an assortment of the strangest instruments imaginable joined in. They had all been improvised with a view to creating as much noise as possible.

Mess tins did duty for cymbals. The drums were skilfully adapted from old obsolete water-containers made of hide. Experts in the art of whistling through closed fists supplied the parts of cornets, flutes, and clarinets. By raising now one finger, now another, they were able to produce a surprising variety of sounds. The result was a remarkable ensemble of military music.

The colonel looked anxious, and the general frowned. But he was soon smiling. He was a sensible man and did not find it improper that men who for a whole year had lived in mud and under fire should give vent to their feelings in such a manner, however irregular it might be. The 1st platoon went on its way in triumph, and the march past continued.

The whole regiment was quartered at Aiello.

That afternoon the mayor regaled the officers with wine and a speech. In a voice trembling with emotion he read: "It is a signal honour for me to have this opportunity . . ." etc., etc. "This glorious war which the people of Italy are fighting under the brilliant and heroic leadership of His Majesty the King . . ."

At the mention of the King we all, as was obligatory, came smartly to attention, with a great clatter of heels and spurs. In the town hall the crash of this military salute resounded like a sudden discharge of firearms. The mayor, simple civilian that he was, had made his modest reference to the sovereign all unwitting of the noisy demonstration of loyalty that it was to provoke. Taken completely by surprise, he nearly jumped out of his skin, and turned a pale and startled face towards the group of officers who were standing rigidly at attention. The sheets of paper from which he had been reading fluttered to the ground.

The colonel could not restrain a smile at the discomfiture of the representative of civil government. He looked proudly from the mayor to us and from us to the mayor, and with that grain of malice that lurks in the heart of even the kindest of men, he determined to give the mayor a further surprise. Sharply his voice rang out:

"Gentlemen, long live the King!"

"Long live the King!" we repeated, in one deafening shout.

But this time the mayor was not to be put out of countenance. He joined with us, and then, picking up the sheets of paper, continued his speech:

"We shall conquer, because it is written in the Book of Fate that we shall be victorious. . . ."

We none of us knew anything about such a book, and still less what might be written in it. In any case the phrase did not greatly impress us. But as the mayor proceeded, we listened with more attention.

"War is not so arduous as we are apt to think it. This morning, as I watched the happy entrance of your battalions into our town, to the accompaniment of the most joyful fanfare imaginable, I realized, as did all our townspeople, that war has great attractions. . . ."

The cavalry lieutenant saluted, with a jingle of spurs, as though this remark were a compliment intended specially for him. The mayor went on:

"Great and sublime attractions. Unhappy are they who know them not! Because, gentlemen, it is a noble thing to give one's life for one's country. . . ."

This sentiment pleased no one, not even the colonel. The quotation might be a classical one, but the mayor was hardly the right person to make us appreciate, even from the literary point of view, the beauty of such a death, however glorious. The very way in which he had spoken the words was unfortunate, for it had sounded as though he meant to imply that we would be better dead than alive. Some of the officers coughed and looked haughtily at him. The cavalry lieutenant clattered his spurs restlessly.

Possibly the mayor realized something of our feelings, for he hastened to bring his speech to an end, with another tribute to the sovereign: "Long live our glorious warrior King!"

The cavalry lieutenant was standing nearest to a large table covered with glasses of wine. Seizing one that was still full, he held it aloft and shouted a ribald remark about the King.

The colonel was staggered, and stared at Grisoni as though unable to believe his eyes and ears. Giving the rest of us a look that seemed to call on us to bear witness to what had occurred, he said in a tone more shocked than angry:

"Lieutenant Grisoni, you have been drinking too much again. Leave the room and await my orders."

The cavalry lieutenant clicked heels, stood at attention, saluted, and said: "Yes, sir."

Then, his riding-crop under his arm, he went out, visibly pleased with himself.

Chapter 2

THE MEN AT THE HEAD OF THE COLUMN SANG:
Quel Mazzolin di fiori . . .
and the rest of the company joined in:
Che vien dalla montagna. . . .

The song cheered the men, who were tired after being on the march for three days. The months of trench life on the Carso had made us unused to prolonged physical effort, and this march was proving exceedingly trying to every one of us. Our only consolation was that we were going up to the mountains. The rest at Aiello had not lasted even a week. The Austrians had launched a big offensive between the Pasubio and Val Lagarina, and after breaking the front at Cima Dodici (Summit XII), were now pressing forward onto the Asiago plateau. Our brigade had hurriedly to leave its billets; having crossed the Venetian plain by train, it was now approaching the lower slopes of the plateau by forced marches.

The men were singing, but the thoughts of each one were following their own course. No more trench

warfare! Now it was to be a war of manœuvre, of attack and counter-attack, so we were told. And at last
we were to be in the mountains. We had always talked
of war in the mountains as though it were almost a
holiday. Now we too were to see trees and woods and
streams, valleys and remote places, that would make
us forget not only our vanished period of rest, but the
horrors of the arid, stony Carso, the Carso which was
everywhere the same, and always the same, without a
blade of grass or a drop of water, with no shelter except
for a few great cavities in the rock known as *doline,*
in which, since they were always a target for the enemy's heavy artillery, lay heaped in ghastly confusion
men and mules, alive and dead. We should be able,
when not on duty, to laze about in the sun, or to sleep
in the shade of a tree, without being awakened by a
bullet in the leg. And from the mountain heights we
should see far-distant horizons instead of the unending lines of trenches and barbed-wire entanglements.
At long last we were to be freed from that wretched
existence at a distance of only ten to fifty yards from
the enemy in a monotonous and ferocious promis-
cuity consisting of continual attacks with bayonets or
hand-grenades. We should be done with killing one
another, day in, day out, without anger, without hate.
A war of manœuvre was quite different. One good
stroke of strategy and two or three hundred thousand
prisoners might be taken in a single day without any
of that frightful wholesale slaughter to which we had

become accustomed. And who could tell? Perhaps we might even win the war and have done with fighting for ever.

The only drawback to this kind of warfare was that we seemed to be always on the march.

A regiment of cavalry crossed our road and we had to halt as they filed past. Lucky devils to be on horseback! But we soon saw that they were no less dead tired than we were.

"Yours is a soft job!" shouted the foot-soldiers to the lancers.

"You're damned lucky to be on your own feet!" they retorted. "We're riding, riding all the time. And with the horses to look after, our work's doubled. What a life!"

When the cavalry regiment had gone by, the company resumed its singing.

The road was now crowded with refugees. Not a living soul had remained on the Asiago plateau. The population was pouring in confusion down into the plain, bearing with it, in ox-carts or on mules, the old people and the children, and such household goods as they had been able to save from their homes. Torn from their land, the peasants were as though shipwrecked. There was no sound of lamentation, but they had a lost look in their eyes. It was like a funeral procession.

Our column stopped its singing, and the men fell silent. Only the sound of our marching and the slow creak and grind of the bullock-carts was to be heard on the road. The sight of refugees was new to us. On the Carso it had been we who were the invaders, and the peasants who had abandoned their homes at our approach had been Slavs. But we had not seen them.

A wagon passed us, larger than the others. Crouching upon two straw mattresses were an old woman, a young mother, and two small children. An old peasant sat in front, driving the oxen. He stopped them and asked a soldier for a pipeful of tobacco.

"Here you are, Grand-dad," called out the corporal at the head of the column, and, without stopping, handed him his whole supply of tobacco.

The men followed his example. The old man, his hands full of packets of tobacco and cigarettes, gazed astonished at such unexpected riches. As though obeying an order, each man as he passed tossed his tobacco onto the cart.

"But what will you have to smoke, boys?" called out the old man.

His question broke the silence. Someone started a light-hearted marching-song in reply, and the column, joining in, continued on its way.

I was watching "Uncle Francesco," who was near me. He was the oldest soldier in the company, a veteran of the Libyan war. The men called him "Uncle" because of his age, and because he was the father of five sons. He was marching in time and singing like the others, but his step was heavy beneath the weight of his pack. His face was expressionless as he sang, his head bowed and his eyes on the ground.

"Open order!" someone cried from the rear. "The colonel's coming!"

I turned and saw the colonel and his adjutant making their way on horseback through the ranks of the column. We were already marching in open order to let the refugees through, and there was little space to spare on the roadway. We had to march still more to the sides, and the colonel was forced to ride with great care to avoid both the carts and the marching men. When he came up to me he said that he was pleased to see the men in such good spirits and gave me twenty lire to distribute among the singers. Noticing "Uncle," he asked me who he was. I told him that he was a peasant from southern Sardinia, and added certain particulars about him.

"A good soldier?" asked the colonel.

"Very good indeed," I replied.

"Here are another five lire, for him."

"Uncle" looked up, realizing that we were talking of him, but went on with his singing, unperturbed. The colonel clapped him on the shoulder and went on. The news of his present to the singers spread instantly, and their voices became more animated.

"*O pescator di Londra . . .*" sang the leader, and the others took up the refrain: "*Bionda, mia bella bionda. . . .*"

"Uncle" was still singing loudly, with head bent.

The refugees looked down on us impassively. The creak of their carts on the stony road made a mournful accompaniment to the gaiety of the song.

At twilight we halted for the night.

It was a warm evening. The men stretched themselves on the ground outside their tents. Some, too tired to talk, lay silent, their hands behind their heads, gazing at the flaming sky. Others were talking together in low voices, or murmuring Sardinian peasant songs. No one stirred except the sentries.

Animation returned as someone came back from the canteen having spent all the twenty lire on tobacco and flasks of wine. In war-time no one thinks of the morrow. Soon the flasks were passing from hand to hand, and the men's voices grew louder.

"The colonel's health!"

"The colonel!"

One young voice stood out from the rest, its tone hostile:

"The colonel, son of a bitch!"

His comrades protested.

"Do you want the colonel to put a bullet into your belly instead of wine?"

Unobserved, I was watching the scene. The young man did not answer; he was lying full length on the ground, and refused to drink. I recognized him. He certainly had no special reason for wishing the colonel ill.

Gradually the voices became lower again. Then

"Uncle Francesco" began to speak, gravely, like a patriarch. The others listened, smoking.

"Never in all my life," he said, "have I earned five lire in one day. I have never even earned five lire in a week. Except, maybe, at harvest-time, scything by piece-work, from early dawn till after sunset."

I went away, for it was time for mess.

Chapter 3

ON THE EDGE OF THE PLATEAU, THREE THOUSAND FEET up, the greatest confusion reigned. We arrived on June 5, by way of the Val Frenzela, proceeding with considerable caution, since no one knew precisely where our troops or those of the enemy were. The regiment took up positions between the outskirts of Stoccaredo and the Gallio-Foza road, my battalion being near Buso, a small village at the end of the valley. The advance posts were on the plateau, near Ronchi, on the roads along which the enemy advance guard might be expected to approach. We knew nothing except that having crossed the Val d'Assa and taken Asiago, they were pressing forward, fanwise, beyond Gallio. But it was said that, between them and us, there were still some lost detachments of our troops. At all events it was clear that the Austrians were exploiting their success to the full; in the Asiago valley many field batteries were to be seen taking up their positions in broad daylight. The Val d'Assa bridge, which had been destroyed by our troops, had been reconstructed by the enemy within a few days. All our artillery had fallen into their hands and on the whole plateau we no longer possessed a single piece. Only from Fort Lisser, an old fortress dismantled in 1915, two 149-mm. guns were firing, and always upon us. Luckily most of the shells failed to explode, and we had no losses.

Our war correspondents subsequently christened this fort "The Lion of the Plateau."

My battalion commander sent me in the direction of Stoccaredo with a platoon. My task was to get into touch with certain detachments of our army thought still to be up there, and to obtain information as to the enemy's whereabouts. He had wanted me to take only a small party with me as escort, but fearing that we might fall into the hands of the Austrians, I had asked for my company. We compromised on a platoon.

The sun was already setting when, to the north of Stoccaredo, we came upon a battalion of the 301st infantry regiment. It was commanded by a fifty-year-old lieutenant-colonel, whom I found sitting at an improvised table, with a bottle of brandy in his hand. He received me in a most friendly manner and offered me a drink.

"Thank you, sir," I said, "but I don't drink spirits."

"You don't drink spirits?" he asked in an anxious tone, and taking out his pocket-book he noted down: "June 5, 1916. Met lieutenant who drank no spirits."

He asked me my name, which I had already given him in introducing myself, and added it to the note. Anxious not to waste time, I told him at once of my orders. But he wanted further details concerning me, and I had to explain that I was not a regular officer, but had joined the army on leaving the university at the outbreak of the war. It was the question of my abstemiousness, however, that chiefly impressed him.

"Perhaps you belong to some religious sect?" he inquired.

"No, sir," I said laughing. "Why should I?"

"Strange. Very strange. Do you drink wine?"

"A little. Sometimes, at meals." And I again asked him for information about the enemy positions. But he refused to be hurried. Having drunk another glass of brandy he accompanied me slowly to an observation post some fifty yards away, taking his glass and his bottle with him.

From the observation post we still had a clear view, lit by the last rays of the setting sun. In the distance, twenty miles away towards the north, was Cima Dodici. In front of it lay the chain of mountains culminating in Monte Zebio, the Gallio ridge, and more to the right, higher than all the rest, Monte Fior. Between these heights and where we stood lay the wide Asiago valley; lower down, and immediately beneath us, the smaller valley of Ronchi.

"Where are the Austrians?" I asked.

"Ah, there you have me. Nobody knows. They're

in front of us. At any moment they may be behind us. It depends on the circumstances. All that is certain is that they are everywhere, and that, except for my battalion, there are no Italian troops left up here."

I made some further inquiries about the highest of the peaks, which he had told me was Monte Fior.

"Our men are still holding it. That at least is certain. The Austrians haven't got there yet. The mountain is over sixty-five hundred feet high, and our commanders call it the 'Key to the Plateau.' "

The colonel pointed out the various positions to me with his brandy bottle. Every now and then he made as though to refill his glass, but each time restrained himself.

"On that mountain," he said, "the General Staff has concentrated about twenty battalions, in order not to lose it, whereas here, at the gateway to the whole area, we're only a miserable handful. The whole thing's madness. But according to the text-books, if you hold the top of a mountain, you can prevent the enemy from entering the valley below. Look, you can see the mouth of Val Frenzela down there. Between it and Monte Fior, as the crow flies, there's a distance of at least two and a half or three miles. If the Austrians force the gateway and enter the valley, a whole army corps can get through without losing a man, while the 'key' is left on the wall. You won't have a drink? Ah, of course, you don't drink."

"But I should have thought that if we have twenty

battalions up there, the Austrians will hardly be able to get through here."

"And how are our twenty battalions to stop them, from so far off? With artillery? But we haven't a single gun, and there can't be any up there, because there are no roads. As to machine-gun or rifle fire, it's no good at that distance. What's to be done, then? Nothing need be done at all. Because, though we may be fools, that's not to say that the leaders on the other side have any more sense. The art of war is the same for everyone. You'll see that the Austrians will attack Monte Fior with forty battalions and all to no purpose. So we shall be quits. That is the art of war."

I found the colonel's conversation interesting, but night was coming on and I wanted to get back before dark. Unfolding my map, I tried to get my bearings.

"You're sure you won't have a drink?" Then, in a mocking tone: "Don't put your trust in maps, young man, or you'll never get back to your regiment. Take the word of an old soldier. I went through the whole of the African campaign. We were defeated at Adowa because we went by maps, and ended up to the west instead of the east. Just as though one were to attack Venice instead of Verona. In the mountains, maps are only intelligible to those who know the district, from having lived in it. And they don't need them."

We retraced our steps to his battalion headquarters, and he sat down again to drink two glasses of brandy, one to my health and one to his own. I thanked him and then started off at the head of my platoon with the intention of returning to the regiment.

The colonel's theories evidently had some truth in them, however, for that evening I lost my way. This would not have happened had I kept to the same track by which we had come, but it was now late and I tried to take a short cut instead of keeping to the long road leading to Buso. The path I had chosen led through a wood, in which it was already almost dark. Here the track forked, and a few yards further on, in broken ground covered with thick undergrowth, we were suddenly met by a burst of rifle-fire. I realized too late that we had borne too much to the left, instead of keeping in the direction of Val Frenzela.

"Take cover!" I called out. "To the right, deploy!"

The men threw themselves on the ground and began to spread out to the right, crawling on all fours. Although under fire, we were protected by the lie of the land and the thickness of the undergrowth, which hid us completely.

"These cursed Hungarians!" swore the sergeant, who was close to me. "They've got me in the arm!"

"Hungarians?" I whispered.

"Yes, sir. I caught sight of one. He had the trefoil on his uniform."

"You must be mistaken," I said; "they are Bosnians."

We had in fact been informed at divisional head-quarters that the enemy advance guard consisted of a Bosnian division. The Bosnians did not wear the trefoil badge.

The platoon had spread out and was firing steadily. The sergeant bandaged his wounded arm, helped by one of the men. The numerical superiority of the troops in front of us was obvious. We were being fired at by at least a company. If they had attacked us, we should have been overwhelmed. I gave the order to fix bayonets and passed the word down that the men were to keep close contact with one another and hold themselves in readiness to counter-attack.

Meanwhile I was growing anxious. My orders had been to make a reconnaissance with the object of getting into touch with our left and obtaining information on the situation, not to become engaged with the enemy. The platoon was merely an escort to guard against any possible surprise attack from hostile patrols and was quite unequal to an encounter such as we had now become involved in. I decided therefore to fall back.

After the first display of nervousness the enemy's fire had died down, and only isolated shots were now to be heard. To cover the noise of our retirement, I ordered a hand-grenade to be thrown. The man nearest me lit a "Sipe," held it carefully in his hand as the fuse burned, and then, springing to his feet, threw it well up to clear the branches of the trees. It exploded as it fell with a noise that echoed through the forest, and the fragments scattered in all directions with a strident screech. It was the first grenade that we had thrown on the plateau. For a moment there was silence in the forest. Then from the enemy lines a deep voice gave the order in Italian to fire.

The firing started again, with renewed intensity. A rocket soared up in front of us, illuminating the forest and the whole of the Ronchi valley. We flattened ourselves against the ground.

"Perhaps the sergeant's right," I said to myself. "They must be Hungarians from the Adriatic coast. The Bosnians certainly don't speak Italian."

The platoon was falling back in detachments little by little, in order not to lose contact. The night was now pitch dark, so that it was very difficult to do this in an orderly fashion, and it was more than an hour before we had got well out of the enemy's range and were able safely to fall in again. The last detachment to come up brought a prisoner with them. They had caught sight of him by the light of the rocket, a solitary figure advancing towards us from the direction of the enemy, with raised hands. I was very pleased. A prisoner was just what we wanted to give us information about the enemy, and I said to the corporal in charge:

"I'll see that you and your men get rewarded for this."

The prisoner, whose rifle had been taken from him,

was standing among his captors, two of whom were holding him by the arm. No one said a word. But even in the darkness and silence the sympathy usual in such circumstances had already sprung up. The victors hastened to give evidence of their goodwill towards the vanquished, and the latter to accept it. The prisoner was already eating chocolate given him by our men, and when, since we were now in safety, I gave them permission to smoke, he accepted a cigarette from one of them. I ordered a roll-call to make certain that none of our party had remained behind, and turned on my electric torch.

"But he belongs to our regiment!" exclaimed the sergeant, who, adjusting the bandage on his arm, was standing between me and the prisoner.

"Who belongs to our regiment?" I asked.

"The prisoner."

"Devil take it," muttered the corporal, between his teeth.

I turned my torch on the man's face. He stared back, bewildered. The cigarette had fallen from his lips. There was no doubt about it; his uniform was the same as ours. On his cap was the number 399, that of our regiment, and his badge was that of our brigade. On his shoulder was the number of his company, the 9th, showing that he belonged to our own battalion.

"What's your name?" I demanded.

"Giuseppe Marrasi," he replied, crestfallen.

I asked him the names of his company and platoon commanders. They were fellow-officers of mine.

"But how did you get here?"

"I lost my way."

"Was it the 9th company that was firing on us?"

"Yes, sir."

Roll-call over, we started off again. I could hear the men talking to their prisoner of a few moments ago.

"That was a sell for you, wasn't it?"

"You thought you'd done with the war, didn't you? You'd have given your eyes for us to have been the Austrians."

Marrasi protested: "No, I tell you, no. . . ."

"The way you bolted my chocolate too! You might really have been an Austrian. I'll see you pay me back all right. . . ."

Chapter 4

OUR BATTALION REMAINED BETWEEN BUSO AND THE Gallio-Foza road for four days, in contact with the enemy's advance posts. The Austrians, who had stopped opposite the end of Val Frenzela, were concentrating all their forces against Monte Fior. This position was defended principally by battalions of Alpini: the Val Maira battalion, the Sette Comuni battalion, the Bassano, and several others whose names I forget. They were all regional battalions, recruited in the Alto Veneto, and were therefore fighting in the neighbourhood of their own homes. There were also an infantry regiment and a few other odd battalions. The 1st and 2nd battalions, which had been relieved by other troops brought up from across the Frenzela valley, were the last to join them. Our adjutant was badly wounded, and I, who until then had commanded the 10th company, was promoted adjutant in his place.

We set out from Foza a little after midnight. Our

brigade commander saw us off. He was to join us soon. One of his sons was fighting in the Alpini.

We climbed the rocky mountain-side by a mule-track, in single file. The noise of the fighting at Monte Fior did not reach us, being carried by the wind in the opposite direction, towards Val d'Assa, and the silence of the night was broken only by our footsteps and the noise of our iron-tipped alpenstocks against the rock. Now and then the pale flicker of distant rockets reached us. From our right, beyond the slopes of Monte Tonderecar, we could hear far-off the raucous bark of a fox, like a sarcastic laugh.

The winding mule-track ended at Malga Lora, a little grassy, open valley beneath the heights of Monte Fior. We reached it just as a column carrying wounded on stretchers was beginning the descent. The little valley lay before us, green and peaceful like an oasis, with patches of snow still remaining here and there between the rocks and in the shade of the bushes. Our battalion was closing up, and the major thought this a suitable place in which to re-form it.

The sound of intermittent rifle-fire could now be heard distinctly. The summit of Monte Fior was only a few hundred yards away, but from where we were we could not see it. The major had spread out a large map and was examining it, smoking as he did so, when suddenly there was a spatter of bullets as two machine-guns from above began to fire down on us. He hurriedly left his map and went to the head of the bat-

talion to make the men take cover. In a moment we
had scattered among the rocks.

After the first surprise, we realized that the enemy
was dominating the mouth of the valley, having apparently seized one of the highest points on the mountain during the night and posted machine-guns there.
But our troops were evidently still holding the lateral
positions, for otherwise no one could have remained
in the valley at all. However, the headquarters of the
Alpini were safely established there and the dressing-
stations, from which the wounded were now coming.
They, too, had now been forced to halt and fall back.

"Take two dispatch-bearers," said the major to me,
"and go and find out what the situation is. Tell the
officer commanding the Alpini that we're here and
are awaiting orders." As usual his speech was accompanied by various oaths. He was a Tuscan, from Flor-
ence, and he swore continually. When excited, he
would make use of the entire vocabulary of the Lung'-
Arno.

Followed by two dispatch-bearers, I ran across the
open ground swept by the machine-gun fire, and in a
few minutes reached cover. The headquarters of the
Alpini could be seen at the far end of the valley,
against the mountain-side. Beside it the Red Cross
flag of the dressing-station was flying over an old
wooden cow-shed. I made my way there and found
the ground about it crowded with wounded waiting
to be evacuated to Foza, while more were coming

down from above. I asked for the officer in command
of the Alpini. He was pointed out to me, standing
apart, wrapped in a big military cloak and gazing fixedly at the heights above the valley.

I presented myself. He was wearing a trench helmet, and his rank was not immediately distinguish-
able, but in giving me his hand he revealed a colonel's
stripes on his sleeve. He listened to me with apparent
calm, despite the lack of sleep apparent in his drawn
face and the messages that he was constantly receiving
from every part of the sector. Beside him sat a captain
of Alpini, writing, without once raising his head.

"We're being shot down and we haven't enough
force to resist. We've no artillery except the guns at
Fort Lisser, over six miles away, which have already
killed one of my officers and some men. We haven't
even a machine-gun. The enemy fire has put them all
out of action."

The colonel made a disconsolate gesture. From under his cloak he drew a metal flask, stared at it as
though anxious to make sure of its identity, and took
a sip. Then he went on: "Last night we were attacked
on the ridge by superior forces. A whole company
was wiped out: the 4th, belonging to your regiment.
Not one officer left. They'd just taken over from one
of my battalions, which was knocked out yesterday
afternoon. Inform your headquarters."

"Very good, sir."

The colonel took another sip from his flask. "Tell

your commanding officer that an attack must be made on the ridge. By bearing to the right you can avoid the ground under machine-gun fire. He must retake the ridge. Is your battalion pretty fresh?"

"Yes, sir."

"Ready for anything?"

"Yes, sir."

The colonel offered me his flask. "Tell your commanding officer that you found me here—that you found Colonel Stringari, of the Alpini, resolved to die."

"Yes, sir."

"Tell him that we've all got to die here. All of us. It's our duty. Tell him that. You understand?"

"Yes, sir."

I ran back again, and reported to the major. When I told him that we had all got to die, he exploded into a volley of oaths.

"We've all got to die, have we? Then let him begin by dying himself. It's his affair. Let's see him do it. Our problem is to live, not die. If we all die, the Austrians will go strolling down to Bassano with their pipes in their mouths. Did you say we'd got to attack the ridge?"

"Yes, sir, the ridge."

"Give me something to drink," shouted the major to his orderly, who handed him his brandy flask.

An attack on the ridge was unquestionably a difficult operation to carry out, but the major, despite his excitable temper, knew his job. It was not impossible that we should succeed in the attempt.

The whole battalion had now come up and every company was reported ready for action. The major sent Lieutenant Santini, of the 9th, with a platoon, to reconnoitre the ground, thinking that, instead of attacking the ridge in front from below, it might be better to work round to the right flank and do so from above.

While preparations for carrying out this plan were being made, a second lieutenant of the Alpini came over to us, bringing with him a written order from the colonel to the effect that the attack on the ridge was to be abandoned and we were to take up positions as quickly as possible on Monte Spill, facing Monte Fior. It was a completely different operation, and Monte Spill was in the opposite direction from that in which we had been about to attack. The major demanded an explanation. The second lieutenant replied that Colonel Stringari feared that at any moment the Austrians might force our positions on Monte Fior and make another push forward. Just after my interview with him the Bassano battalion, reduced to forty men, had been compelled to fall back. Our defences therefore must be strengthened at the most vulnerable point.

The major swore at these orders and counter-orders; but he at once gave commands that the battalion should move off towards Monte Spill.

He was even more irritable than usual that day. He was constantly asking whether the mule with the battalion headquarters baggage had arrived. We had no need of the baggage, and the major's impatience was obviously due to some special cause. I soon guessed that it was his personal baggage he wanted, not that of battalion headquarters. A few of us knew that the major, when under fire, was accustomed to wear a steel cuirass under his uniform. To avoid its weight when on the march, he had evidently left it behind with the rest of his personal baggage, and he was now constantly feeling his chest, as though to make sure the cuirass was not there. He was used to the dangers of war and had been through the whole of the Libyan campaign, in all probability without wearing a cuirass. But this one seemed now to have become an obsession with him, keeping him in a continual state of nervous irritation. The whole valley echoed to his oaths.

We proceeded to climb up Monte Spill, with some difficulty. The ground was rough and covered with scrub. Lieutenant Santini, with a platoon of the 9th company, was ahead, reconnoitring. An enemy patrol, with a machine-gun, fell into their hands. We could not make out how they got there, because in front of us our lines were still holding out. Probably they had come from some other sector and had lost their way. We sent them to the rear, without having been able to understand a word they said. This time they were really Bosnians. This lucky chance had a calming effect on the major, who gave orders that they were all to be given bread and cigarettes.

We reached our positions towards five in the afternoon. Monte Fior was still holding out. Various battalions of infantry belonging to other regiments had also been hurriedly brought up to Monte Spill. A subaltern from one of them saw us and came over to establish contact with us. When he returned to his headquarters, I went with him to find out exactly what forces we could count on on our left. And for the second time I came upon Lieutenant-Colonel Abbati, of the Stoccaredo outpost. He was now in command of two battalions of his regiment, the headquarters of which, with one battalion, was still at Stoccaredo. Like us, he was here under the command of the Alpini.

He was lying full length under an open tent, and seeing me before I was aware of him, he called out to me:

"Come and sit down a moment. Now what did I tell you? You see, the Austrians are attacking Monte Fior."

I sat down on the ground beside his tent. A bottle and a small glass stood within reach of his hand. Once again he asked me about my university studies.

"So you were at Turin University? That's good! Let's have a talk and forget about the war."

He was a Piedmontese.

"War, everlasting war!" he went on. "It's enough to drive one mad. Can I speak openly to you?"

"Of course, sir," I answered. "I'd be delighted."

"I ought never to have been a soldier. Can you honestly say that I've the face of an army officer? I studied literature for two years at the university, and I was always first in my class. That was my real career. But my father had a bee in his bonnet about the army and insisted on my entering the military academy. He was a colonel, my grandfather was a general, my great-grandfather a general, and my great-great-grand-father . . . in a word, I'm descended in a direct line from eight generations of army officers. They've been the ruin of me."

The colonel spoke slowly, and drank slowly, as though sipping a cup of coffee.

"I protect myself by drinking. If I didn't I'd have been in an asylum long ago. An honest man has to defend himself against the iniquity of the world by drinking. I've been fighting now for more than a year, on one front or another, and so far I've not seen a single Austrian face to face. And yet we're killing one another all the time. Killing people we don't know, don't even see! It's horrible. That's why we all have to get drunk, on both sides. Have you ever killed anyone with your own hands?"

"I hope not, sir."

"I haven't. I've not seen anyone to kill. All the same, if we were all, by common accord, to stop drinking, the war might come to an end. But if others drink, I do too. Listen to me. I've seen a lot of fighting. It's not artillery that supports us infantry. Quite the contrary. Our artillery often lets us down, by firing on us."

"The Austrian guns sometimes fire on their own infantry, too, sir."

"Of course. It's the same technique. Abolish the artillery on both sides, and the war will go on. But try to abolish wine and spirits. Just try."

"I've tried already, sir."

"That's merely on your own account, and worse than useless. But suppose your example were to become a general order, universally applied. No one would go on with the war. The moving spirit of this war is alcohol. And that's why the men, in their infinite wisdom, refer to it as 'petrol.' "

The colonel got up, a smile on his pale face. From underneath a heap of papers he drew a book. Waving it in front of my face, he said:

"What's this book? Guess!"

"Army regulations, sir," I hazarded, without conviction, trying to read the title.

"Do you think *I* would read army regulations? You must be mad. Guess again."

I realized it must be some book dealing with his particular taste.

"*Bacchus in Tuscany*," I suggested.

"No, but you're getting nearer."

"Anacreon."

"No."

I tried to think of the name of some other famous devotee of drinking. The colonel held out the book to me. I read: *"The Art of Preparing Alcoholic Liquors at Home."*

"You see," he explained, "with this cursed mountain warfare, it's impossible to carry even a couple of bottles with one, but in this way I can make as much as I like. Of course, there's a lot of difference between powdered alcohol and the real thing, but it's better than nothing."

"A rare art," I commented.

"It may be rare," retorted the colonel, "but you can take my word for it, it's more worth while than the art of war."

At Monte Fior the battle was increasing in intensity.

Chapter 5

"WHY HASN'T THAT IDIOT GOT HERE YET?" DEMANDED the major of me, annoyed that the medical officer had not yet rejoined the battalion. "He'll be setting up the dressing-station at his own home if I don't give him a lesson." The baggage had still not come up, although we had been at Monte Spill more than four hours, and he was getting angrier every moment.

He became positively furious when two carabineers appeared at headquarters with a soldier of the 9th company who had been arrested at Foza for being unable to explain his absence from his unit. Brigade headquarters had sent him back to the front line in this manner, in the belief that it was a case of attempted desertion.

"A deserter in my battalion!" shouted the major. "There's never been a deserter in my battalion. I'll have him shot at once!"

The two carabineers—unless they chanced to be Tuscans—can hardly have heard such swearing in their lives as in the course of those few minutes.

39

The major questioned the arrested man. It was
Marrasi, the "Bosnian." He declared that he had lost
the wallet containing his iron rations, and that, fearing punishment, he had gone back to the company's
last stopping-place, below Foza, in the hope of finding
it. But the major would have none of such explanations. Turning to the carabineers, he demanded:

"Why haven't you shot him already?"

Marrasi was saved by the sudden appearance of the
man with the baggage-mule. The major stopped
questioning him, sent the two carabineers away, and
busied himself with the baggage. I moved off, in order not to embarrass him, taking Marrasi with me.

"You're getting into bad habits," I said to him.
"Today you've mislaid your iron rations, and the
other day you lost yourself. What'll you lose next?"

But Marrasi made no answer.

The major reappeared, smiling, and somewhat increased in girth. He seemed a new being. Seeing
Marrasi and me, he came towards us.

"What do those fools of carabineers mean with
their talk of desertion! If there are any deserters here,
it's themselves, living in comfort behind the lines.
Get back to your company, Marrasi! I don't want any
more nonsense about your iron rations. Buy them,
steal them. They've got to be in place. You understand?"

"Yes, sir."

"Get back to your company, then, and let's hear no more about it."

Just before midnight the battalion was ordered to move up to the front line in full force, with all four companies, the section of engineers, and the machine-gun section. We took up our positions in the dark, in a rather haphazard manner, occupying the ground previously held by the units that had now moved over to the right. We spent the whole night digging.

Our situation was not an easy one, as we perceived at daybreak, when the Austrians opened fire. Our orders were to hold on to our position "by tooth and nail." The phrase, though somewhat literary, expressed our situation pretty accurately. Our trenches were only improvised, being little more than shallow cavities in the bare ground, without sandbags or parapets. In fact, they were individual holes rather than trenches, unconnected with one another, which each man had attempted to dig out, if not actually with his teeth, certainly to a great extent with his nails. We lay as flat as we could, our heads inadequately protected by a few stones or clods of earth. Every time we heard the rattle of the enemy machine-guns or the screech of a shell, we instinctively tried to flatten ourselves still more against the ground.

The enemy bombardment was carried out by all the field artillery on the plateau, and also for the first time by big guns. The latter, of 305 and 420 mm.,

were so far quite new to us, and the passage of their
shells made a special sound, a terrific intermittent roar
increasing in intensity until it culminated in the final
explosion. Columns of earth, stones, and fragments
of human bodies were hurled into the air, to fall again
some distance away. A whole platoon could have
taken cover in the huge holes made by these shells. I
thought of the major's cuirass.

The front line, however, was seldom damaged.
Most of the shells fell behind us, near the two lateral
valleys and round Monte Spill. The ground shook
beneath our feet, as though the mountain were convulsed by an earthquake. Even now, so long afterwards, when, by an involuntary psychological process,
one's memory is apt to throw into relief only those
sentiments most creditable to one and to suppress the
rest, I remember the single dominant thought of those
first moments. It was more than a thought, it was
rather an instinctive urge: to save oneself.

The major and I, with our orderlies and runners,
were in the centre of the line behind a small rock,
from which we every now and then looked out. A
young cadet suddenly sprang to his feet among his
men, turned his back on them, and rushed away. He
was only a boy, in poor health, and it was the first time
he had been in any fighting. Bare-headed, his face
contorted, he was shouting: "Hurrah! Hurrah!" as
the Austrians always did in attacking, though in fact
he knew no German.

The major saw him before I did.

"Shoot that coward!" he shouted to me.

I heard him, but I went on watching the boy, without making a movement. The major did not move either, but continued to yell at me: "Shoot him, shoot him!" The cadet had already run several hundred yards and had disappeared from view, but the major went on repeating:

"Shoot that coward! Shoot that coward!"

To distract his attention I took his brandy flask from his orderly and offered it to him. He seized it with both hands and, rubbing the grime off his lips with the back of his hand, took a long drink.

We were all parched with thirst. Every instant, all along the line, one could see some man roll over and drink from a flask. A few moments of bombardment had been enough to make our mouths and throats feel burnt up and to fill us with a desperate longing for a drop to slake our thirst and to help us curb our frantic impatience. The small amount of brandy issued to us at Foza was already finished. In the midst of the bombardment the men could be seen scrambling to their feet one by one and running to seize a handful of snow from a crevice in the rocks, then returning to their posts. There was nothing else to show that there were still living men in the front line. I had some leaves in my pocket, which I had picked from the trees below Monte Spill, and I began to chew them. Everyone was smoking. No sooner had the major finished one ciga-

· rette than he lit another from its stump.

The shells were now bursting so close to us that I could no longer hear what the major was saying. He took a piece of paper, scribbled a few words on it in pencil, and handed it to me. It read: "Stand up and see what is happening." I got up and looked. The men were all lying motionless, in a long row, but to the right, Lieutenant Grisoni was standing up among the men of his company, his hands in his pockets and his pipe in his mouth. I did not notice anything else.

The bombardment continued, undiminished in intensity, but the battalion held on.

How long it lasted I cannot say. Even at the time I did not know. During action one loses all sense of the passage of time. One may think it is morning when it is really afternoon.

Suddenly one of our machine-guns opened fire. I stood up again to see what was happening. The Austrians were attacking.

Chapter 6

I THINK THAT ALL WHO LIVED THROUGH THAT DAY WILL keep it present in their memories until the very end of their lives.

While our machine-gun was firing, the bombardment stopped. At the same moment the enemy started to attack.

Several battalions advanced in line, in close order, with their rifles on their shoulders, making no attempt to fire. Apparently convinced that after such a bombardment not a man could be left alive in our lines, they came on confidently, singing a battle-song of which we could only catch the chorus: "Hurrah!"

In our own lines officers and N.C.O.'s, bent almost double, were running hither and thither, rallying their men. The bombardment had not caused us many casualties. The major was shouting: "Open fire! Prepare to counter-attack with the bayonet!"

The officers repeated the order and there was a great deal of shouting. The battalion had sprung to life again. The whole line then opened fire. Only

one of our machine-guns was in action, the other having been knocked out by a shell. We could only see
the enemy directly in front of us, but they were evidently attacking simultaneously on our right.

They advanced slowly, being held up by the rough
nature of the ground. Our machine-gun rattled furiously, uninterruptedly. Lieutenant Ottolenghi, the
officer in command of the section, was firing it himself.
Numbers of the enemy were mowed down by it.
Their comrades opened their ranks as they advanced,
in order not to tread on the killed and wounded, and
then closed them again. Still singing, the tide of men
came on.

"Hurrah!"

The breeze was blowing in our direction. From
the Austrian ranks a smell of brandy was wafted to us,
heavy and acrid. We were inundated with it. My
nostrils and lungs seemed filled with brandy.

"Stand by to counter-attack!" shouted the major.

My attention was chiefly directed to the captain of
the 11th company. He was standing up only a few
yards from us, his face black with grime, and his head
bare. In his right hand he held a revolver and in his
left a trench helmet.

"Cowards!" he yelled. "Come on, if you've the
courage! Come on, come on!"

And he turned, now towards the Austrians, now
towards his own men, who, still lying on the ground,
stared at him in astonishment. For it was his trench

helmet that he was aiming at the enemy like a revolver
and it was his revolver that he was trying to put on his
head. The more unsuccessful his efforts were, the
more he shouted and raged. He banged his revolver
on his head with such violence that the blood
streamed down his face.

"Hurrah!"

The Austrians were now only fifty yards away.

"Fix bayonets!" shouted the major.

"Savoy!" yelled the men, hurling themselves forward.

I have never had any clear idea of what happened
then. The reek of that brandy had stupefied me. But
I distinctly saw three men with a machine-gun detach
themselves from the Austrian ranks and take up a
position behind a rock, on our left flank. This rapid
movement was immediately followed by the tap-tap
of the Schwarzlose, as its bullets began to whistle
round us. The major, who was still beside me,
dropped his revolver, threw up his arms, and fell
against me. I made an effort to support him, but fell
with him. He lay motionless, and when his orderly
unbuttoned his tunic, we saw that his chest was covered with blood. The steel cuirass was riddled with
holes.

I got up and ran forward. Our men had already
met the Austrians, and both sides were brought to a
standstill in the ensuing mêlée. The Austrians began
to fall back slowly, having been thrown into disorder

by our unexpected resistance. Our men, prevented from advancing farther by their officers, threw themselves to the ground and opened fire at the retreating enemy. I saw a few Austrians fall before they disappeared behind the ridge. The wind continued to waft waves of brandy over us.

The unfortunate major had given clear orders about the counter-attack. He wished the battalion to reoccupy its original position as soon as the Austrians had been repulsed. I had the order promptly carried out. The officer next in seniority, Captain Canevacci, took over the command of the battalion.

The ground was covered with dead, but we had held on. We carried the wounded back as best we could, for we had no stretchers left. Lieutenant Grisoni, who had a leg smashed, was brought in, whistling, by two of his men. Some sort of order was soon established in our line, and a roll was called.

Hours passed. The sun began to sink, and we still had no news of what was going on elsewhere. Nothing was to be heard of the Austrians except the firing now and again of a few field-pieces. It was the calm that follows a storm.

At last a written order arrived from the officer commanding the sector, to the effect that the enemy had taken several positions, rendering the Monte Fior line no longer tenable. We were ordered to fall back in good order in the direction of Monte Spill.

"Fall back on Monte Spill?" shouted Captain Canevacci, swearing at the runner. "And tomorrow we'll get an order to attack Monte Fior again, and we'll all be blown to bits."

He could not see why we should abandon so important a position without resistance.

"I'm not going to fall back," he kept saying. "I'd rather be shot."

The runner asked for a written receipt for the order, but Captain Canevacci refused to give him one.

"Say I'm not going to give any orders to retire. Say they can have me shot for insubordination, but that so long as I'm in command of this battalion, it's not going to abandon Monte Fior."

I tried to point out to him that only the officer in command of the whole section of the front was competent to judge of the situation, and that we had no possible grounds for assuming that he was wrong. And that, in any case, we had to obey orders. The captain refused to be convinced, and sent the dispatch-bearer back without a receipt. As an officer of the regular army he was taking very grave risks in so doing. I tried in vain to persuade him to change his mind, but he was convinced that to abandon Monte Fior would be no better than treachery. Half an hour later a corporal belonging to our regiment appeared with another written order, this time signed by the colonel himself. "If the battalion," it ran, "does not retire according to orders, Captain Canevacci will be relieved of his command."

"I relieved of my command!" shouted Captain Canevacci. "The Italian army's commanded by Austrians! It's outrageous!"

He was furious. But he had to obey. We fell back company by company, taking the dead with us. As the last company left Monte Fior, the rest of the battalion had already taken up its position between two others at Monte Spill.

A thin line of outposts had been left on Monte Fior to cover the retirement. They had been given orders to fire an occasional round, and to withdraw as soon as the enemy made any attempt to advance. It was late afternoon before the Austrians became aware of our retirement. When at last they suspected it, they sent forward a line of patrols. Our rearguard fired their final rounds and then rejoined the battalion. The enemy patrols found Monte Fior deserted.

I was in the front line, at the highest point of Monte Spill, watching what was happening on Monte Fior. The Austrians were streaming over it. In little less than half an hour the line we had abandoned was occupied by several battalions. The whole crest of the mountain was crowded with troops.

It must have been towards six or seven o'clock when I noticed an unusual excitement in the enemy positions. What could be happening? The men were calling out to one another and waving. Then the whole mass, standing up on the summit, shouted as one man: "Hurrah!"

They were waving their rifles and caps in the air and looking in our direction.

I could not make out what they were all so excited about. It was more than the rejoicing one would expect over a position taken without resistance. Why such enthusiasm?

I turned round, and understood.

Before me, lit up by the rays of the setting sun, lay the whole Venetian plain, spread out like an immense cloak embroidered with pearls. Below us lay Bassano and the Brenta; farther off, towards our right, the cities of Verona, Vicenza, Treviso, and Padua. And in the far distance, on our left, Venice.

Venice!

Chapter 7

OUR DIVISIONAL COMMANDER, WHO WAS HELD RESPONSI-
ble for the unjustifiable surrender of Monte Fior, was
relieved of his command, and Lieutenant-General
Leone took over the division in his place. In an order
of the day he was introduced to us by our army corps
commander as "a soldier of proved courage and
strength of purpose." I came across him for the first
time at Monte Spill, near our battalion headquarters.
His orderly officer told me that he was the new divisional commander, and I presented myself to him.

Standing at attention, I gave him the latest information concerning our battalion.

"At ease," said the general curtly. "Where have
you been fighting up till now?"

"With my brigade, on the Carso, sir."

"Have you been wounded?"

"No, sir."

"What, you've been at the front since the beginning of the war and have never been wounded? Not
once?"

"No, sir, except for a few slight wounds that did not necessitate my leaving the battalion."

"But I mean serious wounds."

"I haven't had any, sir."

"Most extraordinary. How do you explain it?"

"I can give no exact reason, sir, but I've certainly never been badly hit."

"Were you present at all the fighting in which your brigade has taken part?"

"Yes, sir."

"In all the engagements on the Carso?"

"Yes, sir."

"Most extraordinary. Are you by any chance lacking in courage?"

It seemed to me that an army corps commander, at the very least, was needed to deal with a man like this. As I did not answer at once, the general repeated his question.

"I think not," I replied.

"Do you merely think not, or are you sure?"

"In war one can be sure of nothing, sir," I answered gently; and added, with the hint of a smile, in the hopes of propitiating the general: "Not even of being sure."

The general did not smile. I do not think he was capable of smiling. He was wearing his steel helmet with the chin-strap fixed, which gave him a metallic look. His mouth was invisible but for his moustache, and one might almost have thought he had none. His eyes were grey and hard, like those of a bird of prey.

He changed the subject.

"Do you like war?"

I hesitated. Ought I to answer the question? There were officers and men standing round us, listening to what was being said. I made up my mind to answer as best I could.

"I was in favour of Italy's participation in the war, sir, and at my university I was the leader of the interventionist group."

"That," said the general, with terrible calm, "concerns the past. I'm asking you about the present."

"War is a serious matter—very serious, and it's hard to say whether . . ." He was staring at me, evidently dissatisfied. I went on: "At all events, I do my duty. In every way."

"I did not ask you," the general retorted, "whether you did your duty or not. In war everyone does his duty, because if he doesn't he risks being shot. I asked you whether you liked war."

"Whether I like war," I repeated despondently.

The general, inexorable, was staring fixedly at me. The pupils of his eyes seemed to have grown. They gave me the impression that they were revolving in their sockets.

"You can't answer?" he insisted.

"Well, it seems to me—I can say, at any rate, that I . . ." I floundered, seeking desperately for a possible answer.

"Well?"

"That personally, that is, speaking for myself, in a general way, I can't really profess to have any particular *liking* for war."

"Attention!" ordered the general.

I was already standing at attention.

"So you are in favour of peace?" There was surprise and contempt now in the general's voice. "Of peace," he continued, "like some girl, who loves her home and all its comforts. Is that it?"

"No, sir."

"Then what kind of peace is it that you want?"

"A peace—" a sudden inspiration came to my rescue, "a victorious peace."

The general seemed reassured and let me go.

A few moments later he asked me to accompany him to the front line.

When we had reached the highest point of our front-line trench, which, facing Monte Fior, was that nearest to the enemy, he asked:

"What is the distance here between our trenches and the Austrians?"

"About two hundred yards," I answered.

"It's two hundred and twenty," said the general.

"Very likely," I answered.

"It's not likely, it's certain," he retorted.

Our trench was solidly constructed of stones and earth. The men could walk along it upright without being seen by the enemy. Our snipers kept a good look-out, firing through loopholes, from under cover. The general looked through the loopholes, but this did not satisfy him. He had a heap of stones made so that he could stand on it and look over the parapet, with his field-glasses to his eyes. His head and shoulders were thus fully exposed.

"Sir," I said, "the Austrians are remarkably good shots. It's dangerous to expose yourself like this."

The general took no notice, but continued looking through his glasses. Two reports rang out from the enemy's lines, and the bullets whistled past him. Two more followed, still near. Still calm and unhurried, he then got down. I looked at him closely. He had an air of arrogant indifference. Only his eyes revolved, dizzily, like wheels.

One of our sentries, a few paces off, was looking through his loophole, paying no attention to us. But a few men and a corporal of the 12th company had gathered near us in a small group and were watching the general with more distrust than admiration. In the reckless demeanour of their divisional commander they evidently found some cause for apprehension concerning their own fate. He looked at them with satisfaction.

"If you've the courage," he said to the corporal, "do what your general has just done."

"Yes, sir," replied the corporal, and leaning his

rifle against the side of the trench, he climbed onto the mound.

Instinctively I seized him by the arm and pulled him off it.

"The Austrians are on the look-out now, sir," I said; "they won't miss again."

The general, with a furious look, reminded me of the vast difference in rank between himself and me. I let go of the corporal's arm and said no more.

"It's all right, sir," said the corporal, and climbed up again.

Hardly had his head appeared above the parapet when a volley rang out. The Austrians were evidently waiting with their rifles covering the spot. The corporal was not touched and remained leaning over the parapet, his whole chest exposed.

"Bravo!" said the general. "Now you can get down."

From the enemy trenches a single shot rang out, and the corporal toppled backwards onto us. I bent over him. A bullet had gone clean through his chest, below the collar-bone, and blood was trickling from his mouth. With half-closed eyes, scarcely able to breathe, he murmured to me: "It's nothing, sir."

The men were looking at the general with hatred in their eyes.

"He's a hero," said the general, "a real hero," and he bent over the wounded man. As he stood up again, his eyes once more looked into mine. It was only for a moment. But in that moment I remembered having seen those same cold, revolving eyes before, in the lunatic asylum near my home, on the occasion of a visit I had paid there with our professor and other law students from the university.

"He is a true hero," repeated the general, taking a silver lira piece from his pocket. "Here," he said, "drink a glass of wine, when you get the chance." The wounded man made a gesture of refusal with his head, and hid his hands. The general stood with the coin between his fingers and after a moment's hesitation let it drop on the corporal's body. No one picked it up.

Continuing his inspection of the front line, the general reached the end of the section occupied by our battalion and dispensed with my services.

I went back to battalion headquarters. The front line was seething with indignation. The news of what had happened had spread throughout the sector, largely owing to the stretcher-bearers who, in carrying the corporal to the dressing-station, had told everyone they met about the incident. I found Captain Canevacci extremely angry.

"The Italian army is commanded by Austrians!" he exclaimed. "We've Austrians in front of us, Austrians behind us, and Austrians in the midst of us!"

At headquarters I came across Colonel Abbati, who was about to go up to the line with his battalion. He too had heard the story. I greeted him, but he made no response except to remark gloomily to me: "The art of war follows its usual course." Stretching out his arm, he made as though to take the flask that I carried, slung from my belt. I hastened to offer it to him. He looked at it absent-mindedly and, taking hold of it, gave it a shake, to make sure it was not empty; then, removing the cork, he put it to his lips, only to remove it instantly, with a start of surprise. From the look of horror on his face, it might have been thought that he had just tasted poison.

"Coffee!" he exclaimed, in a tone of compassion. "Weak coffee! Young man, you must start drinking or you will end up in a lunatic asylum, like your general."

Chapter 8

IT WAS HARDLY TO BE EXPECTED THAT AN OFFICER SO intrepid as General Leone would remain inactive for long. Despite the fact that we still had no artillery whatever on the Asiago plateau, he ordered an assault on Monte Fior for the 16th of that month. My battalion was in reserve, so I did not take part in the fighting. The enemy artillery and machine-gun fire held up our attack from the first moment, and our regiment alone lost three hundred men and ten officers in half an hour. The general, seeing it was hopeless, was forced to suspend operations.

A few days of calm followed for us. The enemy guns were quiet and we did not have a single casualty. It was a real rest. We spent our time lying in the sun against the rocks, gazing dreamily over the Venetian plain. Life seemed far away from us.

But our divisional commander allowed himself no rest. He wanted at all costs to capture Monte Fior. Every day he was up in the front line, calculating distances, scribbling on maps, making plans. Finally he worked out a scheme consisting in a surprise attack in full daylight, with bayonets, to be carried out by my battalion, which was considered the one most familiar with the ground in question.

The attack was fixed for the 26th. But on the 24th the Austrians fell back, abandoning Monte Fior to us in much the same way that we had abandoned it to them. Our resistance on the Pasubio and the great offensive launched by the Russians in Galicia had forced them to suspend operations on the Asiago plateau. Their retirement, which must have taken some days to carry out, had been cleverly concealed from us. When we discovered it we promptly advanced, but had only a few encounters with scattered patrols that had been left in the front line.

The general was even bolder when it came to a war of movement than he had been in trench warfare. He gave orders that our troops were never, by day or night, to lose contact with the enemy and insisted on our brigade commander remaining in person with our advance parties. Our brigadier, in spite of his advanced age, put himself at the head of the leading company and was killed in a skirmish with enemy patrols. It was a great grief to the whole brigade, for the men were much attached to him.

When General Leone heard of his death his resolution was redoubled.

"He must be avenged!" he announced. "Avenged at once!"

His thirst for revenge became somewhat modified owing to the behaviour of the enemy. Their machine-gun detachments were fighting with dogged persistence, ready to sacrifice their own lives if by so doing they could hold up our advance. In this way a number of machine-guns fell into our hands which had been defended until death by their crews. Other detachments who were still posted on the heights above us forced us to keep in open order and caused us continual delay. The general no longer showed his habitual calm. Climbing a tree, he took up his position at the top of it like the captain of a ship at the masthead, and shouted.

"Forward, men! You must avenge your brigadier!"

"If we were to avenge our brigadier in good earnest," growled Captain Canevacci to me, "we'd have two generals dead today. Our revenge would leave the post of divisional commander vacant once more." And he took no notice whatever of the general's orders.

Even if our men had been imbued with the most heroic ardour imaginable, it could not have failed to be mitigated by the hilarity which the general's exhortations, coming as they did from so strange a position, aroused.

"If the general would only make himself a nest and stay in his tree," remarked Captain Canevacci grimly, "the division would be saved. Once he comes down, we're lost."

Our battalion had moved to the rear of the first-line troops, which had had to spread out to avoid offering an easy target for the enemy machine-gunners and to be ready for any possible counter-attack. We were moving forward slowly, for it was difficult, under fire, to make progress through the forest, in which only rough paths and tracks existed. We had to push through the undergrowth and do our best to keep in touch with the companies on our flanks.

Towards evening enemy resistance weakened. Their patrols were still firing, but they did not wait to be attacked with the bayonet before falling back. We were following up now with greater speed and were not suffering many casualties. The general had come down from his tree and was marching on foot between the 2nd battalion and ours, followed by an orderly leading his mule. From in front of us a voice suddenly cried: "Halt! Ground packs!"

"Who was that?" asked the general, angrily.

It was a private of the 7th company of the 2nd battalion, on liason duty, who, having come to a point where the path forked, had warned the men behind him to stop so that the scouts might have time to find out which was the right track to follow. One of them had been killed only a moment before, and it was clearly unwise to continue the advance without reconnoitring the ground. He was only obeying orders, as Captain Zavattari, of the 6th, pointed out to the general.

"Have that man shot," ordered the general.

Captain Zavattari was an officer of the reserve, and the senior captain in our regiment. In civil life he was head of a department in the Ministry of Education. It seemed inconceivable to him that he could have one of his men shot. He explained this carefully to the general.

"Have him shot this instant!" replied the general, without a moment's hesitation.

Captain Zavattari went away, and having questioned the scout, returned to the general, who immediately demanded: "Have you shot him?"

"No, sir. He was simply carrying out his orders. In calling out: 'Ground packs,' it never occurred to him for a moment that he might be exhibiting slackness or indiscipline. The scouts had just had a man killed, and a halt was necessary to reconnoitre the ground."

"Have him shot all the same," replied the general, in an icy tone. "An example must be made."

"How can I have a man shot when he's committed no crime, and without any sort of trial?"

But the general was only irritated by Captain Zavattari's juridical arguments.

"Give orders at once for a firing party," he shouted, "and don't force me to have you shot too, by my own carabineers."

Captain Zavattari realized that there was nothing to be done unless he could find an expedient for saving the scout's life.

"Very well, sir," he replied.

"Carry out the order and report to me at once."

Captain Zavattari went forward again to his company, which had halted to await orders. He ordered a firing party to fire a volley at a tree-trunk, and made the stretcher-bearers place on a stretcher the body of the scout who had just been killed. He then returned to the general, followed by the stretcher-bearers and their burden. The men, who knew nothing of the reason for so macabre a stratagem, stared dumbfounded at one another.

"The man has been shot," said Captain Zavattari.

Seeing the stretcher, the general came to attention and saluted it proudly. He appeared deeply moved.

"Let us salute our country's martyrs! In war, discipline is a grievous necessity. Let us honour our dead!"

At nightfall we stopped following up the enemy. The advance parties halted, and sent out patrols for protection during the night. My battalion was slightly to the rear across the Val di Nos, on the edge of a wood. A violent hailstorm had reduced the temperature to freezing-point and we were all drenched to the skin. We had a blanket each and a sail-cloth cover, but we were still wearing our summer kit, just as we had on the Carso. The cold was unbearable. At midnight we were allowed to light fires, as the enemy was some way off and the wood hid us from sight.

We were sitting round the fires. The fir branches burned with a resinous smell. The men were discussing in whispers the events of the day. Suddenly a loud shout resounded through the wood.

"Keep a good look-out! Don't go to sleep! The enemy is not far off!"

Who could it be?

"Keep a look-out! Anyone who falls asleep is a dead man. Your general does not sleep. Be on your guard!"

It was General Leone.

His voice echoed through the silence of the night with a cavernous sound. I had just left my place near one of the fires, where I had been sitting beside our battalion commander, and was standing near the men of the 12th company, who were crouching in groups about the blazing branches. They were unaware of my presence among them, having drawn near to one of the fires, to get some warmth from the flames. I was staring in the direction from which the general's voice was coming.

"Keep a look-out! Your general is here. Don't sleep!"

The voice was coming nearer and nearer. The general was walking through our battalion.

"The madman is awake," whispered a private of the 12th.

"Generals are better dead than awake," commented another.

"He's walking right into us," said another man.

"Is no one going to have a shot at that butcher?" whispered the first speaker.

"I'm going to. I'll have a shot at him." The speaker was an oldish man, who until now had said nothing, apparently merely intent on warming himself. He was sitting next the sergeant.

The men were huddled so closely round the fire that the flames lit up their faces, and I could recognize each one. The sergeant was kneeling motionless, his hands held out to the flames. He said nothing.

"If he shows himself, I'll shoot him," repeated the same man. I saw him take up his rifle and load it.

"Keep a look-out! Be on your guard!" shouted the general.

He suddenly became visible, between two of the fires, about fifty paces away. He was wearing his trench helmet and a long grey cloak. A thick scarf was wrapped round his neck and shoulders, and he was walking slowly, shouting, with both hands to his mouth. In the flickering light of the flames he had a phantom-like appearance.

"Keep awake!"

"Curious," I said suddenly, "the general doesn't seem to need any sleep."

The soldier lowered his rifle. The sergeant sprang to his feet and offered me his place by the fire.

Chapter 9

THE NEXT DAY WE CONTINUED OUR PURSUIT OF THE enemy. Our advance troops, having passed Croce di Sant' Antonio, were making their way through wooded country towards Casara Zebio and Monte Zebio. As we advanced, it became evident that the main body of the enemy had stopped on the higher ground. Their resistance had again become obstinate. The last Austrian detachments, with which our patrols were keeping in touch, were clearly being supported by other troops in the vicinity. As progress was very slow, my battalion, having advanced beyond the Val di Nos, remained inactive all day, waiting to be called on.

The second battalion, acting as advance guard, were ordered to halt and dig themselves in, and during the night we took over from them. When we came up, a line of trenches had been hurriedly dug by them at the edge of a wood. In front of them there were only a few scattered firs, but the ground was thickly covered with undergrowth. Some hundreds of yards away, over the tops of the last fir trees, the rocky slopes of the mountains could be seen. It seemed likely that the enemy's chief stand would be made at their foot.

At daybreak Captain Canevacci and I were in the front line with the 9th company, waiting for the machine-gun section, which had not yet come up. The captain in command of the 9th company was keeping a look-out in front of us, with a party of picked snipers. We lay near him, behind a slight rise, Captain Canevacci with his field-glasses to his eyes.

Suddenly, at less than a hundred paces from us, an enemy patrol appeared among the bushes. It consisted of seven men, walking in Indian file, their rifles in their hands and their packs on their backs, evidently quite unaware that we were so near them. They were exposed to view from the knees up. The captain of the 9th company made a sign to his men, who fired, and every man in the patrol fell.

"Bravo!" exclaimed Captain Canevacci.

A party of our men crawled out immediately to bring in the dead and wounded, disappearing from sight into the undergrowth. We waited for their return, but time passed and there was no sign of them. They had evidently had to go forward with great caution for fear of an ambush. Captain Canevacci grew impatient. Moreover, the machine-gun section had still not come up. Fearing that it might have lost its way in the wood, among the other detachments of our men, I went back to look for it.

I found it a third of a mile away near the 2nd battalion, and I arrived just in time to witness a scene of some excitement. Between the machine-gun section and the 2nd battalion I saw General Leone, seated on his mule, slowly making his way up the rocky mountain-side. The mule gave a sudden start just as it was skirting the edge of a steep precipice with a fall of over a hundred feet, and the general slipped from the saddle. The mule, seemingly quite indifferent to him, continued on its way, along the edge, while General Leone, clinging to the reins, was dragged along hanging half over the ravine. At every step the animal gave him a push with its nose, trying to free itself from the encumbrance. At any moment the general might easily have been hurled into space. Numbers of men were watching from near by, but not one of them made a move to help the general. I could see them all clearly. Some of them winked at one another, grinning.

In another moment the mule would have succeeded in ridding itself of the general, when, from the ranks of the machine-gun section, a man rushed forward just in time and caught hold of him. Completely unperturbed, the general, as though accustomed to incidents of the kind, remounted the mule and continued on his way, soon disappearing from sight. The soldier stood looking round him with an air of satisfaction. He had saved his general's life.

When his comrades of the machine-gun section came up with him, they fell on him savagely, raining blows upon him and rolling him on the ground in their wrath. "Wretch! Fool!" The unfortunate man tried to defend himself from their kicks and blows, but he was helpless.

"Let me go! Let me go! Help!"

"Take that! And that! Who paid you to be such a fool?"

"You'd save the general's life, would you? You're in the pay of the Austrians."

"Let me go! I didn't do it on purpose. I swear I didn't do it on purpose."

The officer in command of the machine-gun section was nowhere to be seen. As no one else intervened, I ran towards the group of men myself. "What's happening?" I shouted.

My presence took everyone by surprise. The aggressors scattered. Only one or two remained, standing at attention. I held out my hand to the victim and helped him to his feet. When I looked round again, I saw that we were alone, the few men remaining at my approach having disappeared like the rest. The soldier I had rescued had a black and swollen eye and one side of his face was covered with blood. He had lost his trench helmet.

"What's it all about?" I asked him. "Why did they go for you like that?"

"It was nothing, sir," he stammered, looking nervously about him, ostensibly in search of his helmet, but also out of fear of being overheard by his comrades.

"What do you mean? You've a black eye and your face is bleeding and you say it's nothing? What's the meaning of it?"

Much embarrassed, the man made no reply. I tried again, but could get nothing out of him.

We were delivered from this awkward situation by the arrival of the officer in command of the machine-gun section, Lieutenant Ottolenghi, who had so distinguished himself at the battle of Monte Fior with his one undamaged machine-gun. He and I were equal in rank, but I was senior to him. Nevertheless, without so much as a word to me, he shouted to the unfortunate gunner:

"Imbecile! You've disgraced the section!"

"But what was I to do, sir?"

"What were you to do? What the others did, of course. Nothing. You should have done nothing. And that would have been too much. I won't have an ass like you in my section. I'll have you transferred."

The gunner had retrieved his trench helmet and replaced it on his head.

"You ask what you were to do?" went on Ottolenghi contemptuously. "You wanted to do something, did you? Well, why didn't you cut the general's reins with your bayonet and let him fall?"

"What?" muttered the gunner. "Let the general be killed?"

"Yes, you fool, let him be killed. Since you wanted at all costs to do something, you could have helped him to die. Get back to your section, and if the others kill you it'll be no more than you deserve.

"It's all very well," I remarked, as the soldier made off, "but you really ought to take things more seriously. In a few hours the whole brigade will know about this."

"I don't care whether they do or not. As a matter of fact it's as well they should. It might enter someone's head then to have a shot at that brute."

As he spoke, he put his hand in his pocket and took out a coin. Spinning it in the air, he said to me:

"Heads or tails?"

I did not answer.

"Heads!" he shouted himself.

It was tails. "He's lucky," said Ottolenghi. "If it had been heads— Oh, well, it'll have to be some other time. . . ."

As the machine-gun section rejoined the battalion in the front line, the party sent out by the 9th company was just coming in with the bodies of the patrol that had been shot down. Six of them, including a corporal, were dead, and one was still living. From an examination of their papers we found that they were

Bosnians. The two captains were much pleased, especially the battalion commander, who hoped to be able to obtain useful information from the wounded man. He had him taken at once to the dressing-station, and himself informed divisional headquarters, asking for an interpreter to be sent up.

The six dead men were lying side by side, on the ground. We gazed at them thoughtfully. Sooner or later, we knew only too well, our turn would come too. But Captain Canevacci could not contain his satisfaction. Stopping beside the body of the corporal, he said:

"Ah, if you'd only learned how to lead a patrol properly, you wouldn't be here. On patrol, those in command must, before all else, see . . ."

He was interrupted by the battalion commander, who, his finger to his lips, signed to him to be quiet. A noise that sounded like voices in altercation was coming from the direction in which we had first seen the patrol, but nearer to us. Captain Canevacci peered ahead, and the snipers raised their rifles. The battalion commander and I went silently into the front trench and looked over the parapet.

The sounds were coming from the trunk of a large fir tree, which was lit up by the rays of the setting sun. Two squirrels were leaping about on it, playing at hide-and-seek. With little shrill cries, like half-suppressed laughter, they greeted each other as they bounded to and fro from opposite sides of the trunk.

And each time that they met they sat up on their haunches, chattering, and making little gestures with their front paws, as though paying each other compliments. Their white chests and stiff bushy red tails gleamed in the sunlight.

One of the snipers looked up at the captain of the 9th and whispered: "Shall we shoot them?"

"Good heavens, no," he answered, in surprise, "They're such pretty little creatures."

Captain Canevacci went on with his lecture to the dead Bosnian:

"The leader of a patrol must see and not be seen. . . ."

Chapter 10

THE ENEMY'S RESISTANCE WAS STIFFENING AND THEIR new line becoming more clearly defined. The patrols we sent forward during the day met none belonging to the enemy, whose fire was now coming from a continuous line suggesting trenches already constructed. In several places we had caught sight of barbed-wire entanglements. We did not push forward any farther, and our brigade proceeded to occupy the most advanced positions of the Army Corps.

The day passed quietly. General Leone was planning a night attack on the enemy's lines, and towards evening we had orders to hold ourselves in readiness. We called in the patrols and made preparations for the attack. Barrels of brandy were brought up to us by mules, and we dealt out rations of it to the men.

We were all anxious about this night attack, which was to be carried out along the whole front. How would it go, and what should we find in front of us? Scattered patrols, as the general asserted, or trenches strongly defended, as the glimpses we had had of barbed wire would lead one to suppose? The men drank their brandy and waited, their nerves on edge. Captain Canevacci had already finished his ration and started on mine.

It was ten o'clock. Only a few stars were visible in the sky, and the forest was in complete darkness. The order to attack had still not arrived. General Leone evidently wished it to come as a surprise to us as well as to the Austrians. Our battalion commander had massed his men in column. He had arranged that only one company was to take part in the attack; the others were to move up only if the first had broken through the enemy's defences. We all stood motionless and and silent. Only the noise of one rifle knocking against another, or a mess tin kicked accidentally against a stone, broke the stillness of the night.

The general had had the brilliant idea of making our bugles sound the advance; this, he thought, would fill our men with enthusiasm and the enemy with terror. When the notes pealed out, our troops ran forward. But at the same instant the Austrians, warned by the bugle-call, opened a deadly machine-gun and rifle fire. For a few minutes the noise was deafening. The bugles continued to sound, and the enemy to fire without pause. In front of us hundreds of rockets rose skywards, lighting up the whole of our attacking forces. Our men, mown down by the murderous fire, were forced back without having even reached the enemy line.

The greatest disorder ensued, and the task of bringing in the wounded only added to the confusion. The "surprise" had not come off and the attack had been a failure, but the general made the buglers go on sounding the advance. It seemed as though he were determined to conquer the enemy's positions by the sound of the trumpet.

Some hours later, when calm had been restored, we learned that General Leone was quite satisfied with the results obtained. He had simply wanted to make the enemy reveal their positions and the strength of their forces. It would have been easy enough to discover this by sending out a few reconnoitring patrols, but our divisional commander scorned such obvious means.

Our pursuit of the enemy, therefore, was now at an end. The Austrians had come to a halt and had dug themselves in. There could be no further doubt on that score. By withdrawing from Monte Fior they had shortened their line by about twelve and a half miles and so avoided the danger of encirclement. They were now on the defensive. A new phase was beginning, which would consist in mass attacks with artillery support, instead of skirmishing between patrols and advance guards. All this would need time for development. Perhaps meanwhile we should get a little rest.

So at least we told ourselves. But our general thought otherwise. The unsuccessful night assault had inspired him with an idea for a big attack on the following day.

Our brigade was therefore shifted to positions farther to the left, under Casara Zebio. Four battalions were to carry out the attack, leaving only two in reserve. My battalion was to be on the extreme right flank. For the intended operation we could count on no arms but our rifles. Our scanty allowance of handgrenades had been used up at Monte Fior, and there was not a single piece of artillery to support us. The undertaking appeared one of extreme difficulty. But our troops were in good fighting trim. Cartridges and brandy were sent up to us on mules.

The attack was begun by my battalion, at five in the afternoon. We went forward *en masse,* according to our orders, and as the Austrians saw us the moment we started, we at once came under intense machine-gun and rifle fire. I have only a confused memory of those hours. The distance we had to traverse to reach the enemy's lines was not more than a hundred yards, and the ground was covered with rocks, stones, and low scrub. Our orders were not to halt, and we covered the short distance at the double, in one rush. Captain Canevacci was leading, and was among the first to fall, with a bullet through his chest. The 9th company, too, lost its commanding officer, the last captain left in the battalion. But the attack surged forward. The enemy fire could not reach us all, for the rocks, al-

though low, afforded us a certain measure of protection.

The ground behind us was strewn with dead and
wounded, but all the same the battalion reached the
enemy lines. I had had to leave Captain Canevacci
where he was lying, and found myself beside Lieutenant Santini, who was leading the 9th company in
his stead. A long line of barbed-wire·entanglements
and *chevaux de frise* barred the way to the enemy's
trenches, which were protected by high stone parapets. Standing close to the barbed wire, we too
opened fire. We were now out of the line of fire of the
machine-guns, which, during our rush forward, had
mown us down from positions on our right flank, and
which still continued to fire at the ground behind us.
Only one was firing on us from the front, but Santini
concentrated against it the fire of those of our men
who were near it, and reduced it to silence. Then
from our left, a hundred paces away, another began
to enfilade us. We were unable to get out of its field
of fire and could not even tell its position. We threw
ourselves on the ground, each man taking what cover
was available, and continued to fire at the trenches,
aiming through the loopholes, in the hopes of keeping down the enemy snipers. The line of battle on
all sides prevented us from knowing whether the
troops on our flank had had any more success than we.

How long we remained in this position I do not

know. The barbed wire prevented us from advancing any farther, the machine-gun fire from falling back. We had to stay where we were, motionless and lying flat on our stomachs, firing without cessation at the enemy's loopholes to prevent our being killed ourselves under the wire. We could have held out for some time like this, even till nightfall, and then retired under cover of darkness, had it not been for the machine-gun on our left, which was raking our line. One by one the men were being hit.

Our only hope was to send someone back with a message to the battalion operating on our left, so that the machine-gun could be dealt with. I could not see a single officer except Santini, who was fully occupied in keeping up the fire against the enemy trenches. I therefore crept slowly through the rocks and bushes, making my way towards the left. It took me a long time, because the greatest care was necessary in order not to be seen, and because the battalion on our left flank was farther off than I had thought. The crackle of the machine-gun and rifle fire was incessant. The 1st battalion was still in action, but it was farther back than ours and had the benefit of more cover. There was a continual coming and going of dispatch-bearers and of wounded behind the fir trees. I asked at once for battalion headquarters, and a private pointed it out to me. I ran there at once.

It was installed behind a high rock, and the ground round it was crowded with wounded. Orders, shouts,

and groans were to be heard on all sides. Confusion
reigned everywhere. The major in command of the
battalion was standing under a large fir tree. I knew
him well, having often dined in his mess. Red in the
face, he was gesticulating wildly towards someone I
could not see. He seemed to be furiously angry.
"Quick!" he kept shouting. But no one came.

As I drew near, he went on repeating; "Be quick,
be quick, I tell you, or I'll shoot you! Get me the
brandy!"

He was howling at the top of his voice rather than
shouting, as though giving orders to a whole battalion. Just as I arrived on the scene, an exhausted
orderly appeared, with a bottle of brandy in his hand,
held aloft as though it were a flag. I went up to the
major and saluted. He was grasping his revolver in
his right hand and a sheet of paper in his left. Drop-
ping the paper, he rushed at the soldier crying:

"Give it to me!"

With a lightning gesture he put the bottle to his
lips. Rigid, his head flung back, he might have been
a dead man standing upright. Only his throat moved
as he swallowed the spirit, with great gulps that
sounded like groans.

I waited till he had finished. Slowly and reluc-
tantly he removed the bottle from his lips and gave it
back half-empty to the orderly. I quickly told him
the reason for my coming, but he made no reply. He
was staring at me, but his thoughts were far away and

he evidently heard nothing of what I said. His revolver was still in his hand, and to show that he was at least aware of my presence, he pointed it at me. I moved it aside, fearing it might go off, and he let me do so, but immediately aimed it again in my direction. I took hold of his wrist, removed the revolver, emptied it, and gave it back to him. He did not utter a word, but took it from me with complete indifference. Then he gave me a smile, but it seemed to me as though it were not he but a stranger smiling. He appeared to be conveying to me that he had only been joking. Since he was speechless and I was wasting time, I went off hoping to find the adjutant.

The adjutant had been killed, the other officers were all engaged in the fighting, and the men attached to headquarters could not get to them, nor did they know where they were. All around, the whistle of the machine-gun bullets went on uninterruptedly, like a hurricane. Branches of trees, sawn off by the fire, kept falling to the ground with an ugly, tearing sound.

Having hurried in vain hither and thither, I retraced my steps to go back to my battalion, and passed the headquarters again. The major was still just as I had left him, motionless, his revolver in his hand. He was still smiling.

Chapter 11

THAT NIGHT WE MADE OUR WAY BACK IN SCATTERED groups to the line from which we had started the attack. Every officer in the battalion except Santini and myself had been killed. Ottolenghi was all right, but he had not taken part in the assault, having been ordered to stay behind with the machine-guns. Our losses amounted to about half our strength. We spent the whole night bringing in the dead and wounded, and when, after roll-call, Santini and I were able to exchange a few words, it was all we could do not to throw ourselves into each other's arms.

So we were back at trench warfare once more. Our dreams of a war of manœuvre and of victory had vanished. It was to be the same thing all over again, just as on the Carso.

A few days of quiet ensued. The brigade had to be reconstituted. Every day drafts of men were sent up and new officers arrived. Gradually the dead were forgotten as the old hands and the fresh arrivals made friends with one another.

We constructed our trenches at a distance from the enemy varying from fifty to a hundred yards, according to the lie of the land and the cover afforded by the fir wood. They were to be our homes; the Austrians, now on the defensive, were certainly not likely to attack them. But we had to be exceedingly careful, all the same. On the other side were picked snipers who never missed their mark. They did not fire often, but always at the head, and they used explosive bullets.

These quiet days passed all too quickly. The battalion had been hurriedly reconstituted, and further operations were announced for the near future. Every day we received consignments of ammunition, and cylinders of high explosive, the big cylinders, two yards long, that we had had on the Carso for destroying barbed-wire entanglements. Wire-cutters arrived also. Neither they nor the explosives had ever been of the slightest use against the enemy's wire, but, all the same, they kept on coming. And brandy too, in large quantities. We were obviously on the eve of another attack.

It had been decided at headquarters that the next assault was to be preceded by a lavish use of these cylinders, which were to be exploded under the enemy's wire on the night before the attack. At the point chosen for the assault my battalion was to go forward together with the first battalion of the 400th regiment. This battalion, like ours, had suffered serious losses, but had been reconstituted. The major in command of it had recovered. He sent Lieutenant Mastini over to discuss with me a common plan of action for placing the cylinders in position.

Mastini and I had been at the university together. He was younger than I, but we were great friends and, both on the Carso and since, we had seen each other often.

Having finished a tour of inspection in the line, we stopped behind the trenches for a talk. I stretched myself on the ground and he sat on a rock, in the shade. Our conversation turned to the subject of his commanding officer, and I told him of the episode in which I had taken part during the last engagement. Mastini too was of the opinion that the major drank too much.

"He's not a bad officer," he said. "He's often courageous and sometimes even intelligent. But during an engagement he's incapable of moving a step without brandy."

"Do you remember Pareto?" I asked him. "How he drank! He must have been one of the most brilliant students at the university, but without drink he couldn't pass an exam. Rather like your major: no brandy, no fighting."

Our talk drifted into reminiscences of our student life, which seemed to us so far away that it might have been a dream. We recalled a certain *festa* in which we had taken part and which had become famous because the wine had been less innocuous than it appeared, and the Rector of the university had burst into song, while a girl student had embraced the prefect's wife.

"But you too drink a lot now, don't you?" I asked him. "They say that everyone in your battalion drinks like a fish."

His only answer was to unsling his flask, as though my question had suddenly reminded him of its existence, and drink a few sips. The brandy was certainly exceedingly strong, as I could tell by the pungent smell that reached me.

"I like Homer's *Odyssey*," he remarked, "because with every book another wineskin makes its appearance."

"Wine," I pointed out, "not brandy."

"Yes," he observed, "curiously enough, in neither the *Odyssey* nor the *Iliad* is there any mention of spirits."

"Can you imagine Diomedes," I asked, "having a good swig from a flask before going out on patrol?"

Our minds were half in Troy and half on the Asiago plateau. I can still see my friend as, with a smile of kindly scepticism, he drew a large steel case from his pocket and offered me a cigarette. I took one and lit both his and mine. He was still smiling as he considered how to reply.

"All the same," he began, and paused; then with a puff at his cigarette, he went on: "All the same, if

Hector had had a spot of brandy, of really good brandy, perhaps Achilles wouldn't have found things so easy. . . ."

In my mind's eye I saw Hector pause in his headlong flight and, in full view of his fellow-citizens upon the ramparts, take an elegant brandy flask from the gold-embroidered leather belt that Andromache had given him, drink from it, and turn to face Achilles.

I have forgotten many things that happened during the war, but I shall never forget that moment. As I watched my friend's face, a single shot rang out from the enemy trenches. Mastini bowed his head, his cigarette still between his lips. From a red mark on his forehead a thin stream of blood trickled out. Slowly he toppled over and fell across my feet. He was dead.

That night we were to put the high-explosive cylinders in position. There were ten of them at battalion headquarters, trussed up like tree-trunks. They were all to be exploded beneath the enemy wire, and as the younger officers had not seen them used before, Santini and I were put in charge of the operations. It was not a difficult job to anyone accustomed to patrol duties; even if there were firing going on from the enemy lines the risk was not great. But steady nerves were needed.

Volunteers were called for and from among those who offered themselves we chose the men we wanted.

Each one was to receive a reward of ten lire from regimental headquarters. Two men were needed for each
cylinder, making twenty of us in all. We were divided
into two parties. "Uncle Francesco" was among the
volunteers, and I took him with me.

The men in my party had all fought on the Carso
and I did not have to tell them what to do. At the time
ordered, after the men had drunk their brandy ration,
we left the trench, my group on the left, Santini's on
the right, and spread out fanwise till we were all about
ten paces from one another. The enemy line was
about fifty yards away.

To those unaccustomed to such work it is rather
alarming going out like this into the open, under fire
from the enemy sentries. The novice thinks: "I've
been seen. That shot was aimed at me." But it is not
so. The sentries fire at random, into the darkness.

It was a murky night. "Uncle" and I went forward
carrying our cylinder between us. We walked when
it was safe to do so, and crawled on all fours where
there was no cover. The Austrian sentries were firing
at regular intervals. We did not know where the bullets were going, for not one came anywhere near us.

A rocket rose in front of us, then another to our
right, then another.

Was it an alarm? I wondered. We held our breath
and stood motionless until the last rocket fell spent to
the ground. The firing went on slowly as before.

They were routine rockets. We had not been seen. We were walking very quietly, pausing every other moment to listen. The sound of our footsteps was covered by that of the rifle-fire. Our men too were firing, to distract the enemy's attention, but in the air, so as to avoid hitting us. We had to go forward with the greatest care, for it was not impossible that an enemy patrol might be lying behind the bushes. The Austrians sent up more rockets, but as we did not move they could not see us, for it was impossible to distinguish us from the tree-trunks and bushes among which we were standing.

At last, on all fours, we crept up to the barbed-wire entanglements. By the light of a distant flare I could just see beyond the barbed wire the parapet of the trench with its loopholes, looking like dark gashes. To avoid the fire from one of these loopholes I had to move over a little towards the left. But we were still so near it that after each shot I could hear the clink of the empty cartridge-case as it was ejected onto the stony ground.

We were just pushing the cylinder under the barbed wire when about fifty yards to our right a brilliant light shone out, accompanied by a tearing explosion. The first charge was going off. It was evidently Santini's; we had arranged that the first, whether his or mine, should not be exploded before three, and my wrist-watch showed that it was just three o'clock. San-

tini was more punctual than I. Stones and splinters
hurtled all round us. We flattened ourselves still
more against the ground.

The alarm had been given. Dozens of rockets rose
into the sky all along the line, and machine-guns
opened fire. A second explosion followed, then a
third. The flares increased in number, in all directions. The sentry near us kept his head and went on
firing calmly into the darkness. But farther off the
rifle and machine-gun fire became furious. The front
line must have been quickly manned.

"Uncle" gave no sign of life, but the faint smell of
his cigarette reached me. He had lit one before leaving our trench and was keeping the lighted end in his
mouth. Smoked in this way, the cigarette lasted
longer and its light could not be seen. He was going
to set fire to the fuse with it. I turned and saw him
stretched out on his back, gazing up at the sky, no
doubt enjoying the display of fireworks that the Austrians were giving us gratis. He can never have seen
a better one, even in honour of the patron saint of his
own little mountain village. The whole sky was criss-
crossed by the rockets, which lit up the trunks of the
fir trees so that they looked like the columns of a great
basilica.

We got the cylinder under the wire. Taking advantage of the first moment of darkness available, I
crept backwards, leaving my place to "Uncle," who lit
the fuse with his cigarette. Together we took shelter

behind a tree-trunk and waited for the explosion.

Half an hour later we were back in our own line. All ten cylinders had been exploded. We had a roll-call and found no one was missing. One of Santini's men had been wounded in the leg.

Before rejoining their various sections, the men finished the brandy issued to the volunteers.

Chapter 12

NEXT DAY THE 1ST BATTALION ATTACKED. THE AUS-trians, warned by the explosions during the night, were ready for them. Their machine-gun fire mowed our men down, and the battalion never reached their objective. All that day the cries of the wounded echoed in the narrow valley.

Without the help of artillery it was hopeless to think of taking positions so strongly defended. The 2nd battalion made another attempt, but in vain. We all began to lose heart. The men regarded the arrival of the cylinders of high explosive with horror. Putting them out at night meant an attack on the morrow. These were days of gloom and depression.

To accustom the enemy to these nocturnal explosions, the cylinders were then put out every night for a whole week, without any attack being made. Our headquarters thought that in this way, if the wire were once destroyed, a surprise attack might be carried out at last. But by now so many men had been killed or wounded during the laying of the charges that very few volunteers were forthcoming for the work. Finally they had to be ordered out in rotation. "Uncle" always volunteered, and always came back unscathed; but at last he, too, failed to return one night. His body was brought back later by his companion. At the quartermaster's office an account of his earnings was found. Every day he had sent the ten lire of prize-money to his family. Poor "Uncle" Francesco! Those of his comrades who had been with him from the first obtained permission to accompany his body to the cemetery of Gallio, and I went with them. How few we were! There was little left of the brigade that had fought on the Carso.

Our battalion was now commanded by Captain Bravini, a new arrival. He was a young regular officer and threw himself with great energy into the task of reorganizing the battalion. After a couple of days he, too, began to drink, at first in secret, then openly. In the end he used to come and ask me for my ration of brandy as though it were a treasure.

After exploding so large a number of cylinders an attack obviously had to be made. During these days Major Carriera, who commanded the 2nd battalion, was promoted to the rank of lieutenant-colonel. The task of directing the operation in our sector fell to him, and my battalion was placed under his orders for the action. He was a very keen officer, and General Leone thought highly of him, while he in turn had a great admiration for the general. The two seemed, in fact, made to understand each other. From the moment in which he had been put in charge of the plans for the attack, Major Carriera scarcely slept day or night. He wanted to set a great example of efficiency. He was altogether tireless. After a night without sleep he would spend an hour doing setting-up exercises, and insisted that his adjutant should do the same. The latter, who was far from strong, ended by breaking down in health altogether.

Colonel Carriera's plan was to start by exploding more cylinders at night; then at dawn to send forward parties with wire-cutters to widen the breaches in the barbed-wire defences, and immediately afterwards to attack. The only new departure, therefore, was the introduction of the wire-cutters. When I heard them referred to, my heart sank. On the Carso we had lost our best men by sending them up to enemy entanglements with wire-cutters. But Captain Bravini, who, though himself in command of a battalion, was below Carriera in rank, carried out all the latter's orders without raising any objections.

That night the cylinders were exploded. I had carefully hidden the wire-cutters belonging to my battalion, and when, at daybreak, the colonel asked for them, Bravini tried in vain to find them. The search had to be given up.

The colonel called his own adjutant and said to him:

"Have we any wire-cutters in the 2nd battalion?"

I hoped that he would say no, for I had already warned him. He too had been on the Carso and knew well enough what to expect from the use of wire-cutters. But after considering for a moment, he answered:

"Yes, sir, we still have seven, of which five are in good order. Three large and two small."

Then he seemed assailed by doubts. Taking out a note-book, he glanced at it and corrected himself: "Of which four are in good repair. Two large and two small."

He was a Bolognese, a teacher of Greek in civil life, and was always extremely precise in matters of detail, however insignificant.

I was standing near him, and said to him scornfully, in a low voice:

"You and your wire-cutters! Are you trying to get promoted, or what?"

"I'm trying to do my duty," he replied calmly.

The wire-cutters, all seven pairs, were brought out at once. The first glimmer of early dawn was beginning to light the sky, but we could still hardly see one another.

"Captain Bravini," ordered the colonel, "will you send out an officer and two men to examine the barbed wire and enlarge the breaches with the wire-cutters."

The captain ordered Lieutenant Avellini of the 9th battalion to take two men and go out. Avellini was a young officer of the regular army who had recently joined the battalion. Without a word, he took the wire-cutters, handed a pair to each of the men, and, keeping one for himself, leaped out of the trench. All three disappeared towards the enemy's lines.

A few minutes passed without a sound, except the usual firing of the enemy sentries.

"They can't cut the wire until it's light enough for them to see what they're doing," I pointed out to Captain Bravini, "and if it is, the Austrians will see them and shoot them. You can only do a job like that if the enemy trenches are empty."

Captain Bravini's nerves were on edge, and he did not answer. He knew well enough how difficult the operation was. He had already drunk half a flask of brandy.

From the enemy's trenches a sudden volley rang out, and then the whole line opened fire. Our men had evidently been discovered, but from where we were, we could not see what was happening.

"There's no doubt that they're firing on our men," I said in a low voice to Bravini. "It's a hopeless business. It can't be done either by day or by night. The only way to deal with wire is by artillery fire. Without artillery we shall never be able to get through."

Captain Bravini agreed, mechanically. He seemed glued to his flask.

The colonel too was nervous. He was walking up and down the trench, without speaking, followed by his adjutant, like a shadow.

Suddenly Avellini appeared from among the bushes, close to us, with one of his men. Removing some sandbags, we helped them in. The private was wounded in the leg. Avellini had had his tunic shot through in several places, but had escaped without a scratch. He reported to the colonel that the other man had been killed, that the gaps in the entanglements made by our high explosive charges had been blocked by the Austrians with *chevaux de frise,* and that the wire could only be penetrated in one or two places, and only by one man at a time. He added that the alarm had now been given by the Austrians, and that the wire-cutters would not cut.

There were some rolls of barbed wire in our trench, and he tried his pair on a piece of it to show us how they failed to grip. The colonel was annoyed He too tried, but only succeeded in hurting his hand.

The adjutant picked up a pair of wire-cutters that were lying on the ground and tried them in his turn. "But these cut perfectly," he said in triumph.

"Do they really?" asked the colonel.

"Perfectly, sir," repeated the adjutant, and tried them again, with success.

"Then," said the colonel, "we must make another attempt."

"But it's not a question of whether the wire-cutters cut or not," I urged, going over to the captain; "if they were the best in the army, the situation would be the same. The Austrians are waiting now at the gap in their defences and will fire point-blank at anyone approaching them, whether they have wire-cutters or not."

"I am in command here," said the colonel curtly, "and I have not asked for your opinion."

I made no reply and Captain Bravini did not say a word. Then the colonel asked him to send out another officer of our battalion. Without raising any objection, he suggested Lieutenant Santini, adding that no one knew the ground better than he did. Santini was sent for. By now day was breaking and we could see the whole line of the enemy trench. It was obvious that Santini was to be sent to his death quite uselessly.

Again I risked an objection. "It's much lighter now," I pointed out, "and Santini has already been out once tonight, with the explosive charges. Couldn't this be put off till tomorrow night?"

Bravini did not dare to reply. The colonel gave me a furious look and said: "Stand at attention and hold your tongue!"

His adjutant was still going round with the wire-cutters, pointing out to everyone, both officers and men, that they were in perfect condition.

Lieutenant Santini, followed by the orderly who had been sent to fetch him, came up. The colonel explained what he wanted done and asked him if he would volunteer for the work. Santini was very courageous, and I was afraid that he would agree at once. Coming behind him, I gave him a nudge and whispered: "Say no."

"It's an impossible job," said Santini to the colonel. "It's too late now to do it."

"I did not ask you whether it was late or early," retorted the colonel; "I asked you whether you'd volunteer."

I gave Santini another nudge from behind.

"No, sir," he replied.

The colonel looked at him as though he could not believe his ears. He stared round at us all and then exclaimed: "This is cowardice!"

Santini promptly replied, with some heat: "You asked me a question, sir, and I answered it. It's not a matter of cowardice or the reverse."

"You won't volunteer, then?" demanded the colonel.

"No, sir."

"Very well, then, I order you—I say, I order you— to carry out my instructions, and at once."

The colonel spoke quietly, almost as though he were asking a favour of Santini, but his eyes were implacable.

"Very well, sir," answered Santini; "if you give me an order, I can only obey."

"But an order like that can't be carried out," I said to Bravini, hoping against hope that he would intervene. He remained speechless.

"Take the wire-cutters," ordered the colonel, his voice still quiet.

The adjutant came up with the wire-cutters. As he passed me I called out to him, unable to restrain myself: "You might at least go out yourself, with your cursed wire-cutters."

The colonel heard me, but he turned to Santini and said:

"Go on."

Santini took a pair of wire-cutters, and taking from his belt an Austrian dagger with a horn handle which he carried as a trophy of war, he gave it to me and said: "Keep it in memory of me." His face was pale. Drawing his revolver, he jumped over the parapet. The orderly, whom none of us had noticed since his arrival with Santini, took another pair of wire-cutters and followed him.

I was still standing with the dagger in my hand, and Captain Bravini was drinking from his flask. I hurried to the nearest loophole. It was already day.

They were both going forward without attempting to take cover, but the Austrians did not fire at them. The distance between the lines at this point was not more than fifty paces. There were a few trees, and the bushes were low. Had they crawled on all fours they could have reached the entanglements without being seen. Santini put his revolver back in its case and went on with only the wire-cutters in his hand. The orderly was still beside him, carrying a rifle. They crossed the short space between the lines and stopped at the barbed wire. No one fired at them. My heart was hammering against my ribs. I turned and looked down the trench. Everyone was at the loopholes.

How long those two remained standing in front of the barbed wire I do not know. Santini repeatedly signed to his companion to go back. Perhaps he thought his life might be spared. But the very gesture he made seemed one of discouragement. The orderly stayed by his side.

Then Santini knelt down and began to cut the wire. The orderly did the same. A volley rang out, and they both fell.

From our lines we opened a futile and unavailing fire from machine-guns and rifles. I left my loophole and went in search of the Bolognese schoolmaster.

"Now that you've had so conspicuous a success, you and your strategist of a colonel," I said to him bitterly, "you can go and have a good breakfast, thoroughly pleased with yourselves."

He made no answer, but looked at me sorrowfully. There were tears in his eyes. But I was so incensed that I could not contain myself.

"You ought to go out now yourselves, with your wire-cutters, and finish the work Santini and his orderly have begun."

"If I'm ordered to go," he replied, "I'll go at once."

The colonel's plans for the attack to be made at eight that morning by both battalions were completed when the general in command of the regiment and the brigade commander came up to the front line and told him that it was to be postponed.

That night further consignments of brandy and high explosives were sent up to us. An attack therefore was to be made after all. The enemy still had to be "followed up."

Chapter 13

AFTER ANOTHER UNSUCCESSFUL ATTACK BY THE 1ST
battalion, we had a few days' truce, which both sides
employed in strengthening their lines. It was now the
middle of July. Our artillery was beginning to make
its presence known on the plateau. A motorized battery made a sudden appearance on the Gallio road,
fired a hundred shells or so on to our own line, and
then vanished. We never heard any more of it. The
men christened it the "phantom battery." By way of
reprisal the enemy, too, shelled us heavily that day,
and our brigade commander was badly wounded.

My battalion received fresh drafts of officers and
men and was reorganized. A captain and four sub-
alterns were appointed to each company. Captain
Bravini of the 10th company, being the senior officer
in the battalion, continued to command it pending
the arrival of an officer of higher rank.

The Army Corps on either side of us had also suffered serious losses and reverses at Monte Interotto,
Monte Colombella, Monte Zingarello, and other

points. The whole of our army on the plateau had been in action. The "following up" of the enemy, on which General Leone had concentrated in his own particular way, was in accordance with the orders of the General Staff.

Preparations for a fresh attack were being made, and news reached us of the arrival of a group of batteries. My battalion was warned that it was to lead the assault on the enemy's lines, and was ordered to make further reconnaissances. We were not told the exact date of the action.

I think it was on the 16th of July that I received an order to take the officer in command of the 9th company along the front line and give him all the information available concerning the lie of the land and the disposition of the enemy trenches on our sector. He had arrived at the front on the morning of Santini's death, and had in fact been a witness of the incident from our trench. He had been deeply shocked by it. Our battalion commander had issued new orders for the attack and as, according to these, the 9th company would be called on to go over the top first in the forthcoming action, it was incumbent on its commanding officer to find out all he could about the sector of the front line in which he would soon have to operate.

I found him at the headquarters of his company, which was in reserve, behind the front line. He was drinking and seemed to be in a good humour. He knew of the preparations that were being made for the next attack, and I told him of the arrangements made by our battalion commander.

"I know," he said; "now it's my turn to go first over the top. One by one we all get killed."

"This time we shall have artillery support," I said, to cheer him up.

"We shall have the enemy's artillery against us," he retorted, "and there are barbed-wire entanglements everywhere. . . . There's no point at all in my studying the ground. What does it matter whether we attack to the right or the left? It's all the same to me whether I die in one place or another. Still, since it's the battalion commander's wish, come along."

It must have been about five in the afternoon. My intention was to take him along towards our right flank, to the highest point of our line. From there the whole of the ground between our trenches and those of the enemy was clearly visible, and in particular in the direction of Monte Interotto, the line of barbed wire, and the section of trenches that the 9th company would have to attack. It was here that we had constructed the best observation post in the whole of our sector, loophole No. 14, on a high rock facing at an acute angle towards the enemy lines. It was no good for observing either the ground directly in front of us or that on our right, towards Carara Zebio. But, despite the distance, it commanded the enemy's trenches lower down, towards the left, so well that one could watch the Austrians moving about both in their front line and in their communication trenches. I had been up there every day and had been able to make some observations that had proved of use to regimental headquarters. The line was occupied at this point by the 12th company.

We had inspected most of the line and were approaching loophole No. 14 when we met an orderly officer from the 12th coming towards us. I asked him to come with us to the observation post.

"It's no longer possible to make use of it," he said; "at any rate, not by day. The Austrians have spotted it and are keeping a fixed rifle aimed at it. Yesterday we had a sentry killed and this morning one was wounded. The company commander has ordered the loophole to be blocked up with a stone during the day."

"What a pity!" I said. "I had hoped we might have a good look at the enemy trenches from there. We shall have to make the best of the other loopholes."

"You can't really see much from them," returned the orderly officer. "But I've made some sketch maps which I'd be glad to show you. They show the lie of the land precisely as it is to be seen from loophole 14."

"I can't be bothered with sketch maps," exclaimed my companion. "I'll have a look from loophole 14."

"But the company commander has given express orders that it is not to be used," exclaimed the other.

"Well, I shall use it," retorted the captain. And he strode off up the trench, in search of No. 14.

"Get hold of your commanding officer," I said to the orderly officer. "Tell him that the captain in command of the 9th company is here, that he has been drinking, and Heaven knows what he may not do."

A runner was quickly sent off to company headquarters, and we hurried after the captain of the 9th. We came up with him just as he reached the observation post. He tried at once to remove the stone blocking the aperture. Seizing him by the arm, I said: "If the officer in command here has given an order, we ought to obey it."

"And who am I? Am I not his equal in rank?" he retorted, authoritatively.

It was all over in a few seconds. The captain of the 9th was standing directly in front of the loophole. With a rapid movement he pushed the stone aside and looked through. A shot rang out and he reeled and fell. An explosive bullet had smashed his right jaw and shot away most of the side of his face.

That night I was returning from a tour of inspection of the front-line trenches with Lieutenant Avellini, who had taken over command of the 9th company. On our way we passed a large shelter built against the side of a rock, and noticed a glimmer of light showing through some gaps in the sacking that protected it. I stopped and, looking through a hole, saw about thirty men sitting or lying on the ground, smoking, by the light of a single candle.

"Let's see what they've got to say about the company commander's wound," I whispered to Avellini. We went up to the sacking and listened.

Several men were speaking.

"There'll be another attack tomorrow."

"I bet there won't!"

"Why not? Weren't we all born unlucky?"

"I know there won't, because the fatigue parties haven't brought up any chocolate or brandy."

"It'll come later, when we're dead. And the quartermaster sergeant will pocket the lot."

"I tell you no. There's never been an attack without an issue of brandy and chocolate. They might cut out the chocolate, but never the brandy."

"You'll see. These fellows will get us all killed, without either!"

"That's right. They like us hungry, thirsty, and downhearted, so that it's all one to us whether we're alive or dead. The worse it is for us, the better for them."

"That's true enough."

"Yes, that's the truth."

"Don't be a fool! You stuff yourself all day and do nothing but grouse. And now it's chocolate you want. What about those iron rations of yours? If you don't return them, you'll see what'll happen to you. I want no trouble in my section."

"And who pays you to play the spy?"

"If the captain hadn't been knocked out today, he'd

have slit open your belly to get those rations."

"I don't intend to fight without my brandy."

"And where am I to get hold of a couple of cans of beef?"

"You'll do the fighting all right, brandy or no brandy, the same as ever."

"You can get them where you like, as long as you *do* get them. Pinch them. Are you too fat and lazy even to pinch things at night?"

"I spotted a couple of kegs of brandy this morning!"

"They weren't brandy. I got a taste of the stuff. It was rifle-oil!"

"I know I shall have to do the fighting even without brandy. If I don't I'll get shot. And that's what you're after."

"They'll end up by butchering the lot of us, with or without brandy."

"Well, they get killed too. They say the general's been badly hit."

"So much the worse for him. But he's paid to be a general, isn't he?"

"They get killed right enough, but anyhow they die in comfort. Steak for breakfast, steak for dinner, and steak for supper."

"Yes, and drawing enough every month to keep my home going for two years."

"You'll see! He won't die. People like that don't really die."

"They're well enough off, anyway, even when they're dead."

"If they were all dead, we'd be better off too."

"But if we all pass out, the war'll be over."

"We ought to kill off the lot of them."

"But we can't even kill off the divisional commander. We're the unlucky ones. What are we good for?"

"Nothing!"

"Nothing at all!"

"I was told the captain said he wasn't going to lead his men to the slaughter like a lot of cattle. He preferred a bullet through his head!"

"Who told you that?"

"That's what they were saying in the company, when they brought him through on a stretcher."

"We ought to kill the lot of them, from the captains up, or we'll all be done for."

"What about the battalion commander?"

"He only thinks of his career, like the rest of them. But his time'll come."

"They all want to get on. Their gold braid only means so many men killed.

"They say Lieutenant Santini left a will."

"I heard that too."

"So did I."

"And what's in it? Was he married?"

"Married? Not he! The will said: 'I advise my men to shoot the lot, as soon as they get the chance.'"

"Now, he was a good officer."

"Not afraid of anything."

"And he had no more luck than any of us."

"The lieutenant in charge of our platoon wouldn't get himself killed for our sake. He's frightened to death."

"Well, aren't you?"

"No. Not if I can get a tot of brandy."

"If you couldn't, you'd have deserted long ago!"

"Deserted? Where to?"

"Who'll give me a nip?"

"What of? Brandy? A cartridge, if you like!"

"Half a cigar for a sip."

"We'll see about that!"

"All right."

"All right."

"Quiet! There's someone out there."

"There's half for you."

"Quiet!"

We had been leaning up against the shelter, on the side leading to the approach trench. On the other side, at the entrance to the shelter, the company quartermaster called out: "Five men for fatigue duty, to fetch chocolate and brandy!" Then he went on again, without waiting for a reply:

"There you are. Just what you wanted. Chocolate and brandy!"

"Well, pigs are always fattened for the slaughter."

"They're fattening us all right!"

Chapter 14

THE DIVISIONAL COMMANDER, GENERAL LEONE, WAS
directing all the preparations for the forthcoming attack in person. From early morning onwards he was
always to be found in the front line, accompanied by
the regimental commander. The general liked to see
to everything himself. His tenacity of purpose was
even greater than his daring. This time he was determined to break through.

Rumours had spread during the night that a number of batteries of different calibre were to take part
in the operations. So those accursed trenches and
barbed-wire entanglements were going to be blown
up for us at last by the artillery! It was high time, for
since the episode of the "phantom battery" not a gun
had been heard on the whole plateau.

The field guns could not be said to be arriving *en
masse*. However, General Leone was determined to
produce one at least for our benefit. He had a 75-mm.
gun brought up to our line. A fatigue party had
dragged it up to the front by way of mule-tracks and

mountain paths, and it reached us soon after the arrival of the general himself. It was a Déport armoured field gun, and in its solitary state it seemed like a dignified official representative of the rest of its kind. Where its companions were, none of us ever discovered. Probably they too had been sent like ambassadors extraordinary to the various brigades scattered over the plateau. They must have remained silent, however, for we heard nothing of them.

Artillerymen and infantry made a wide breach in our trench and ran the gun into it so that the wheels were outside and the carriage inside the trench. As soon as the Austrians saw it, they opened fire. The gun, with its armoured shield, was not damaged by rifle-fire, and the general ordered the lieutenant in command of the artillerymen to give the order to load and then to fire.

The general, the colonel, Captain Bravini, and I were standing near, under cover of the trench. After the first few rounds General Leone, his usual grim expression unchanged, began to rub his hands together with satisfaction, looking round at the man as though to say: "See what your general has brought you!" The men seemed indifferent, as though unable to appreciate the importance of the gift.

As soon as the gun got into action, enemy machine-gun and rifle fire diminished and then stopped altogether, except for a single expert sniper who was posted directly opposite. Aiming with care, and getting better and better with practice, he tried to pick off the gun-layer by firing through the sighting aperture in the shield. The artilleryman increased the rate of fire, and the noise of the gun, together with that of its shells bursting on the enemy's trench, drowned the small, persistent crack of the rifle. The general was still rubbing his hands together.

"Well done!" he said to the artillery lieutenant. "Well done!"

From the Val d'Assa, not less than four miles away, a battery of 152's began to fire on us. In a few moments a veritable hail of shells was falling round the gun. The gunners took no notice of them, but stuck to their work. Some of the shells fell in front of our trenches, and others on those of the enemy. Our gun had found a useful auxiliary. The general's enthusiasm increased.

"Bravo!" he said again to the artillery lieutenant. "I'll get you promotion for service in the field."

The sniper's aim was becoming more and more accurate. He was firing methodically. A shot finally penetrated the aperture and smashed the gun-layer's arm. Without speaking, he showed it to the officer, who took his place at the gun. The sniper went on as before.

The battery of 152's ceased fire, apparently satisfied. Our gun continued firing, but its shells were falling now on the enemy's barbed wire, now on their trenches, without the slightest effect. It was clear that it could have gone on all day with the same result.

The colonel, who up till now had been standing silently at the general's side, exclaimed, half to himself: "All this is perfectly useless."

The general did not appear annoyed. He turned to the colonel and said: "Do you really think so?"

"No use at all," replied the colonel, positively, "absolutely none, sir."

I looked at the colonel in astonishment. It was the first time that he had ever dared to disagree with an officer higher in rank than himself.

The general reflected for a moment. He stroked his chin and appeard to be deep in thought. He, too, could not fail to see that the little 75 was utterly impotent against such solid trenches and extensive barbed-wire entanglements. While he considered the matter, the artillery lieutenant, too, was hit in the arm. A sergeant promptly replaced him, and the gunners mechanically continued their work.

As the lieutenant passed us, bandaging his arm, the general suddenly seemed to make up his mind. Clapping him on the shoulder, he ordered him to cease fire. Then, turning to the colonel, he said:

"Now we'll try the Farina cuirasses."

I looked at my watch; it was past eight.

Eighteen Farina cuirasses were thereupon brought into the trench. It was the first time I had seen them. They were quite different from the cuirass worn by my former major, which had been very light and made of small steel scales, covering only the chest and abdomen. The Farina cuirasses were of thick armour plating, made in two or three pieces, to cover the neck and shoulders and to protect the body almost as far as the knees. Each one cannot have been less than a hundred pounds in weight. A helmet, also extremely heavy, went with each cuirass.

The general stood looking at them. Since the first fleeting satisfaction that he had betrayed at the firing of the gun, his face had remained as composed as ever. With a scientific air he began his explanations:

"These are the famous Farina cuirasses, which very few people know about. They admit of the most daring exploits in broad daylight. It's a pity there are so few of them—only eighteen in the whole army corps. But all those eighteen are ours!"

A group of men standing a few yards away in the trench heard him, and one of them remarked: "I'd rather have a flask of decent brandy myself."

"To us alone," continued the general, "has the privilege been given of possessing these cuirasses. The enemy have rifles, machine-guns and artillery, but with a Farina cuirass one can get through anywhere."

"Anywhere, that is, relatively speaking," commented the colonel, who seemed in a heroic mood that day.

The general took no notice, only looking at the colonel as though he had raised some technical objection. The colonel was slow and passive by temper-

ament, but once in a while he would allow himself to
go beyond the limits imposed on others. He had the
stature of a giant and a large family fortune—two
qualities not without their effect.

"I have already come across some Farina cuirasses,"
he went on, "and they didn't make a very good impression on me. But perhaps these are better."

"Certainly they're better," replied the general.
"With these one can go anywhere. The Austrians
. . . " he lowered his voice and glanced suspiciously
at the enemy trenches, to make sure he could not be
overheard. "The Austrians have spent enormous
sums in trying to steal from us the secret of how to
make them. But they haven't succeeded. The captain
of engineers who was shot at Bologna had sold himself
to the enemy, it appears, on account of these cuirasses.
But he was shot in time. Colonel, will you be so good
as to order out the working party?"

The party had been formed the previous day, and
consisted entirely of volunteers, including the sergeant. In a few minutes they fell in in the trench,
each with a pair of wire-cutters. They put on the
cuirasses, the general himself giving a hand in tight-
ening a buckle here and there.

"They look like mediæval warriors," he remarked.

We were silent, and the volunteers did not smile.
They got ready hurriedly, with a determined air.
The other soldiers watched them anxiously.

I followed what was happening with apprehension,

remembering the cuirass worn by the major at Monte Fior. It was true that these were much more solid and might afford greater protection than his. But what, after all, could these men do, even if they succeeded in getting through the barbed wire and reaching the enemy line?

We made another breach in the wall of the trench. The sergeant saluted the general, who responded gravely, standing at attention, and then led his men out of the trench. They walked slowly, owing to the weight of the steel, with their heads bowed to protect their faces, for the helmets covered only their heads, temples, and the napes of their necks. The general remained standing at attention until the last of them had left the trench, and then said gravely to the colonel:

"The Romans owed their victories to their cuirasses."

An Austrian machine-gun started to enfilade the party from the right. Another immediately opened fire from the left. I looked at the men around me in the trench. Their faces were contracted with grief. They knew well what was happening. The Austrians was waiting at the gaps in the wire, and the sappers were under a cross-fire from two machine-guns.

"Forward!" shouted the sergeant to his men.

One after the other they fell, every one of them. Not a single man even got so far as the enemy's wire.

"Forward . . ." the sergeant repeated, over and

over again, as he lay wounded in front of the barbed
wire.

The general was silent. The men in the trench
looked at one another aghast. What was going to happen to them now?

The colonel went up to the general and said: "Have
we got to attack at nine all the same?"

"Certainly," replied the general, just as though he
had foreseen that things would turn out precisely as
they had. "My division will attack along the whole
of its front line at nine sharp."

Captain Bravini took me by the arm and said:
"Our turn now!"

He removed the stopper from his flask and drank
the whole of its contents.

Chapter 15

THE ONLY RESULT ACHIEVED BY OUR FIELD-GUN HAD been the wounding of the artillery officer and one of his men. The working party had all been shot down. But the attack was to take place all the same. The general was still there, like an inquisitor, determined to be present and to see with his own eyes that the sentence was fully carried out. It was now a few minutes to nine.

The battalion was standing ready, with bayonets fixed. The 9th company was massed round the breach through which the working party had gone out, and the 10th was waiting to follow after. The other companies were drawn up in close order in the communication trenches and behind the rocks. Not a whisper was to be heard. The only movement to be seen was that of the brandy flasks, up and down, from belt to mouth and from mouth to belt, like shuttles on a great loom.

Captain Bravini had his watch in his hand and was following the inexorable passing of the minutes.

Without looking up he shouted:

"Ready for the assault!"

Then he repeated:

"Ready for the assault! Officers, to your places!"

The voice of the wounded sergeant could still be heard crying: "Forward! Forward!"

Wide and staring, the men's eyes seemed to seek ours. They met only mine, for Captain Bravini was still gazing fixedly at his watch. I forced myself to smile and whisper a few words to them. But those questioning eyes, so full of anguish, appalled me.

"Ready!" shouted Bravini again.

Of all the agonizing moments of war, those just before an attack are the most terrible. To attack! Where was one going? Out into the open, away from the cover afforded by the trenches. Machine-guns, stuffed with ammunition, were lying in wait. Those who have not been through such moments do not know what war is.

Captain Bravini's words seemed like the blows of an axe. The 9th company was standing to, but I could not see all of the men belonging to it, because they were partly hidden by the parapet of the trench. The 10th was directly in front of me and I could distinguish every man. Two of them moved, and I saw them, one beside the other, place the barrels of their rifles under their chins. One leaned forward, pressed the trigger, and slipped to the ground. The other did the same. Was it cowardice, or courage, or madness?

The first of them had been through all the fighting on the Carso.

"Savoy!" shouted Captain Bravini.

"Savoy!" repeated the men.

It was a cry that sounded like a lament and a despairing cry for help. The 9th company, led by Lieutenant Avellini, sprang through the breach and ran forward. The general and the colonel were at the loopholes, watching.

"Headquarters staff to go with the 10th," shouted Captain Bravini, and as the 10th reached the opening, we went forward. The 10th, 11th, and 12th followed at a run. In a few seconds the whole battalion was in front of the enemy trenches.

Whether we had shouted or not, the enemy machine-guns would have been ready for us. Hardly had we crossed a rocky strip of ground and, coming out into the open, begun the descent towards the valley when they began to fire on us. Our shouting was drowned by their firing. It seemed to me that at least ten machine-guns must be sweeping the ground about us. The men who were hit fell heavily.

For a moment I was overcome by mental torpor, and my whole body became slow and heavy. "Perhaps I am wounded," I thought. But I could feel no wound. The firing of the machine-guns and the tread of the men behind roused me, and I suddenly grew fully conscious. I was not aware of anger or hate, but simply of calm, complete and absolute, a form of infinite tiredness together with a quite lucid mind. Then the sense of fatigue disappeared too, and I ran forward again, quickly.

Now that I was calm again, I could see all that was going on around me. Officers and men were falling with their arms flung wide and their rifles hurled so far in front of them that it seemed as though a battalion of dead men was advancing. Captain Bravini never stopped shouting: "Savoy!"

A subaltern of the 12th, red in the face, passed near me, clutching his rifle. He was a republican, and disliked the monarchial war-cry that we used in attack. Seeing me, he shouted: "Long live Italy!"

I had my alpenstock in my hand. I waved it to him in reply, but could not utter a word. Had the ground over which we were running been level, not a single one of us would have reached the enemy wire. We should all have been mown down by their machine-guns. But it sloped slightly downwards and was covered with bushes and rocks. The machine-guns were forced continually to alter their elevation and change their aim, with the result that their fire lost accuracy. Nevertheless, our force was rapidly diminishing in number, and out of a battalion a thousand strong, only a few men were still in a position to carry on with the attack. I looked towards the enemy's trenches. The Austrians were not firing from behind their loopholes. They were standing up and could clearly be seen above the top of the trench. So sure of themselves did they seem that some were even right up on the parapet. They were all firing at us, taking aim as calmly as though practising in a rifle-range.

I stumbled against the wounded sergeant of the working party, lying on his side in his cuirass, his helmet shot clean through. He had been struck in the head while urging his men on and was still mechanically repeating his cry of "Forward! Forward!"

Three of his men lay near by, their cuirasses smashed to pieces.

At last we reached the enemy's trench. As we did so, I saw Captain Bravini fall with outflung arms, against a bush. I thought he had been killed, but soon afterwards I heard his voice repeating hoarsely, at intervals, the cry of "Savoy!"

The battalion was supposed to be attacking along a front of from two hundred and fifty to three hundred yards. But the slope of the hillside had brought us all, as we advanced, involuntarily to the same strip of ground, hardly more than thirty yards in width, opposite the enemy trenches. The machine-guns could no longer reach us, but we offered a solid target to the Austrians as they stood facing us in their trenches. The whole lot of us that remained were concentrated at that one point, and they were firing on us at point-blank range.

Suddenly they stopped. I saw those nearest to me staring wide-eyed and with a look almost of terror, as though it were they and not we who were under fire.

One of them, who had no rifle, shouted in Italian:

"That's enough! Stop firing!"

"That's enough!" repeated all the rest, along the parapet.

The man without a rifle seemed to me to be a chaplain.

"That's enough! You're brave men. Don't let yourselves be shot down like this!"

We stopped for a moment. We did not fire, nor did they. The man who seemed to be a chaplain was leaning so far over towards us that I could have touched him had I stretched out my arm. He was gazing fixedly at us.

From our own trenches a harsh voice called out:

"Forward, men of my glorious division! Forward against the enemy!"

It was General Leone.

Lieutenant Avellini was a few yards from me. We looked at each other. He said:

"Come on."

I repeated: "Come on."

I had no revolver in my hand, only my alpenstock. It never entered my head to use my revolver. I threw my stick at the Austrians, and one of them caught it. Avellini had his revolver. He tried to get over the barbed wire by walking along the trunk of a fir tree that, uprooted by a shell, had fallen over it. He was balancing on it as though on a plank, and was making very slow progress. Firing his revolver, he shouted to his men: "Fire! Why don't you fire?"

A few of them fired.

"Forward! Forward!" yelled General Leone.

Avellini was walking slowly along the trunk, trying hard to keep his balance. Behind him two of his men were attempting to follow his example. I noticed a place where it seemed to me possible to get through the entanglements. There was, in fact, a narrow passage through the wire. But after a few paces I found the way was blocked by a *cheval de frise*. It was impossible to go any farther. I turned round and saw that some men of the 10th had followed me. I stayed where I was, unable to go on. No one fired from the enemy trenches. In front of me I could see a man staring at me though a large loophole. I could only see his eyes. They seemed so big that he appeared to me to be all eyes. Slowly I took a few steps backwards, still watched by those great eyes. The eyes of an ox, I said to myself.

I got out of the barbed wire and went towards Avellini. Several men were now on the tree-trunk, holding on to one another. As I came up, an authoritative voice rang out in German from the trench:

"Fire!"

A few shots were fired. The trunk rolled over, and the men fell off it, backwards. Avellini was not wounded, and replied with some shots from his revolver. We all threw ourselves on the ground and took cover behind the bushes and fir trees. The attack was over. It has taken some time to describe, but it cannot have lasted more than a minute or so.

Avellini was near me, and whispered: "What are we to do now?"

"Stay still and wait for dark," I answered.

"But the attack?" he insisted.

"What's the good of talking about the attack?"

The Austrians continued to fire, but over us. We were safely under cover. Captain Bravini's voice reached us faintly, still repeating: "Savoy!" I went on hands and knees to look for him. It took me an hour to get to where he was lying, stretched out with his head behind a large stone and one hand over his face. He was without his tunic, and one of his arms was bandaged and soaked with blood. He must have bandaged it himself. All round him lay the bodies of his men. The bushes hid him from view, and I got quite close to him before he saw me. When he did, he gave me a long look and said again, in a low voice: "Savoy!"

I put his finger against his lips, to suggest silence to him. Crawling alongside him, I whispered in his ear: "Keep quiet!"

He seemed to wake from a deep sleep. Then of his own accord he put his finger to his lips, and did not speak again. It was as though I had touched some mechanical device and stopped him.

The whole valley was quiet now. Our wounded no

longer cried out, and even the sergeant of the working party could be heard no more, sunk in the depths of eternal silence. The Austrians had stopped firing. The sun beat down on the little battlefield. So the day passed, a moment of time and an eternity.

When at nightfall we returned to our own lines, the general insisted on shaking hands with all the officers; there were only five of us, including the wounded. He said to Captain Bravini: "You can count on receiving the silver medal for conspicuous gallantry in the field."

Bravini remained standing at attention until the general had gone. Once he was alone with us, he sat down and wept the whole night, unable to speak a word.

When we had finished bringing in the dead and wounded, which the Austrians allowed us to do without firing a shot from their trenches, I lay down and tried to sleep. My head seemed light as air, almost as though I were breathing with my brain. I was utterly exhausted, but I could not sleep. The professor of Greek came to speak to me. He was very depressed. His battalion had attacked farther to the left and, like ours, had been all but destroyed. He spoke with his eyes half-closed.

"I'm afraid of going mad," he said. "I *am* going mad. One day or another I shall kill myself. It's the only thing to do."

I did not know what to say to him. I, too, felt waves of madness approach and retreat from me. At times my brain felt as if it were being shaken up and down in my head, like water in a bottle.

Chapter 16

GENERAL LEONE WAS INDEFATIGABLE. HE WAS MEN-tioned in the orders of the day, and this distinction spurred him on to further exploits. Day and night he was to be seen in the front line, and it was quite clear that he was meditating fresh operations against the enemy. But the brigade had suffered too heavily and could not be used again until it had been reorganized. There were no more than two hundred men left in my battalion, including Ottolenghi's machine-gun section, which during the last action had remained in the line; and we were reduced to three officers. Captain Bravini, whose wounded arm had not been considered serious, died. Another officer, who was wounded in the foot, had to be taken to hospital for an operation.

The end of July and the first fortnight of August were a quiet and comparatively pleasant time for us. There were no attacks, and without attacks life in the trenches, however hard it may be, is nothing really to complain of. The whole drama of war lies in the moment of attack. In itself death is a normal happening and soldiers die without fear. But the thought of death, the certainty of its imminence, make the hours that precede it tragic. Why was it that the two men of the 10th battalion had killed themselves? In ordinary trench life no one expects death or thinks it inevitable; and when it comes, it comes in kindly fashion, unheralded and unexpectedly. In any great city there are more deaths through unforeseen accidents than there are in the trenches, in time of war. And just as hardship is thought little of, so even the most dreaded diseases are looked on as of no account. Even cholera itself is not feared. We had an outbreak of it in the 1st and 2nd armies, with many deaths, but the men only laughed at it. What is cholera compared with the enfilading fire of a machine-gun!

Those quiet days in the trenches were almost happy. The men sat in the shade and sang. For the hundredth time they re-read letters received from home; they carved bracelets from copper taken from shell-cases, deloused themselves contentedly, and smoked.

A few newspapers arrived occasionally and we passed them from hand to hand. But they only annoyed us, for they all described the war in so curious a way that we found it quite unrecognizable. The valley of Campomulo through which we had passed after the Battle of Monte Fior, without seeing even one wounded man, was described as "choked with corpses." Austrian corpses, of course! It appeared, too, that we attacked to the sound of music, and that war was, for us, one long delirium of song and victory. Our army journals, too, were extremely irritating. We alone knew the truth about the war, for it was there before our eyes.

One day Second Lieutenant Montanelli came to see me. He had been in the 2nd battalion since the beginning of the war and was now in command of a section of sappers. He had studied engineering at the University of Bologna and we had known each other ever since the days on the Carso. Like me, he was one of the few who had come through the fighting on the plateau unscathed. He found me reading.

"You're reading?" he said to me. "Aren't you ashamed of yourself?"

"Why shouldn't I read?" I asked.

He was dressed in a mackintosh, buttoned up to the neck. Of what he wore, only this and his trench helmet, his puttees, and his boots were to be seen, the last badly split, and held together by a twist of wire. Their soles were new, made of bark from a fir tree. Unbuttoning his mackintosh, he showed me that he was naked from his tin hat to his puttees. Two months of campaigning had reduced him to that. Since the beginning of June not a single garment had arrived in the first line. We were all more or less dressed as vagabonds.

"What's happened to the rest of your clothes?" I asked.

"I didn't think them absolutely essential," he replied, "so I've done away with them. I had to spend so much time hunting for the fauna that they harboured that I thought it best to burn the lot. Now I feel more of a man. That's to say, more of an animal. And you can sit there reading? I'm sorry for you. I suppose it's the life of the spirit that appeals to you. But it's a queer thing, the spirit. Did primitive man have a life of the spirit? All we want to do is to live."

"But in order to live you haven't necessarily got to burn your shirt," I objected.

"To drink brandy and live. To sleep and live and drink brandy. To stay in the shade and live—and drink more brandy. And think of nothing. Because if we were really to think, we should have to kill one another and so finish everything once and for all. And yet you can read!"

I had found a number of books one night that had been left behind at the Villa Rossi, a house standing in a wood half-way between Gallio and Asiago. Owing to the fact that I was on patrol I had not had much time to make a choice, and in my hurry I selected Ariosto's *Orlando Furioso,* a book on birds, and a French edition of Baudelaire's *Fleurs du Mal.* The book on birds had lost its first few pages, so I never discovered the author's name. I kept these books with me during the whole time that I was on the plateau. Sometimes they would be rescued by me and sometimes by my orderly, but I always managed to hang on to them. Probably mine was the only peripatetic library in the army. My orderly had a real passion for birds, being a keen shot, and that book, which was illustrated, was his one diversion. He hardly knew how to read, but in any case it was the pictures that chiefly interested him. We used to read together and exchange views.

"What have you found there?" I would ask him.

"It's a very interesting book. It doesn't make you laugh as much as *Bertoldo and Bertoldino* does, but it gives you more to think about. Every bird there is is in it—not one's missing. Even warblers. Now, I don't say I don't like small birds done with polenta, as they eat them hereabouts, and warblers are very good like that. But, for all that, I prefer roasted blackbirds and thrushes."

"It seems that thrushes come from Germany—though not all of them," I said.

"They can come from wherever they like," he answered, "but they're all the same on the spit. They're all good to eat. Oh yes, sir, thrushes are wonderful eating, if the spit is wood; but, for Heaven's sake, never be so rash as to use an iron one. Use nothing but wooden spits—and never more than once. Every thrush should have his own. And be sure they're made of some soft wood. The first thing to do is to make sure the wood's right. Bite it and see what it tastes like. I always used to do that."

We must have been the only assiduous readers on

the plateau. And since my orderly, whenever he was off duty, used to ask for the book about birds, I was reduced either to Ariosto or Baudelaire. But they were enough to keep me occupied.

It was in this way that I became familiar with these two most characteristic representatives of Occidental culture. It is true that I knew them already, but only superficially, as one gets to know writers whom one reads casually at home, in time of peace. They had made no very special impression on me; but to read them while resting in war-time was another matter. Ariosto was rather like our war journalists: he described hundreds of engagements without ever having seen a single one. Yet what a graceful and delightful world was peopled by his heroes! Certainly he had a sceptical side, but it was wholly coloured by optimism. He is the very genius of optimism. Great battles are, for him, delightful excursions into a blossoming countryside, and even death itself appears to him a pleasant continuation of this life. His captains may be killed, but they go on fighting all the same, not realizing that they are dead.

Baudelaire is very different. The sunlight on the plateau seemed made to illuminate his gloomy life. Like the student from Bologna, he might well have wandered naked on the hills, drinking nothing but brandy. He might even have fought in the war side by side with the lieutenant-colonel I had met at Stoccaredo. Like him, and thousands of my companions, he would have had to drink to blunt his senses and forget. Life was to him what the war was to us; yet how his pessimism is lit up every now and again with the joy of living!

It was a sunny day; the whole front was quiet, except that, borne by the wind, the sound of an occasional shot reached us from the Val d'Asta. My orderly, his rifle on his knee, was bent over his birds, and I was sitting near him, deep in the fortunes of Angelica and Orlando. A cheerful voice suddenly broke in upon our silence.

"Good morning!"

It was a young cavalry lieutenant. I closed my book and stood up. We shook hands and introduced ourselves. It appeared that he belonged to the "Royal Piedmont" regiment and was attached to army headquarters. This was the first time he had come up to the lines; until now he had never so much as seen a trench. Yet even on this occasion he was not on duty, but had come of his own initiative to have a look at the front line and our mode of existence there. He was accompanied by an orderly from the regimental headquarters. He was elegantly, indeed impeccably dressed, with white gloves, a cane, yellow cavalry boots, and spurs.

"You'd better look out," I said to him at once, "for in that bright new uniform of yours you'll be a target for all the expert snipers in the enemy lines."

He joked about these snipers, and about my book.

He wanted to know who had written it, and confessed that he had never read Ariosto. I handed the book to my orderly, got my walking-stick, and rejoined him.

"Orlando is wonderful," I said, by way of making conversation.

"Yes," he replied, "he really ought to be Prime Minister."

"I don't quite see him as Prime Minister," I objected, "but he'd command the army no worse than General Cadorna does."

"Oh, no. His Excellency has no military experience; but he's certainly the greatest orator and politician in Parliament."

"His Excellency?"

Things were becoming involved. During the brief explanation that ensued, I realized that while I was speaking of Orlando Furioso, the hero of Ariosto's epic, my cavalry friend thought I meant Signor Orlando, deputy in Parliament and Minister of Justice in Boselli's Government. The lieutenant was a Sicilian, like the Minister, and had an unbounded admiration for him; however, he extricated himself with self-possession from an embarrassment which flattered my feelings as a mere infantry officer. Even my cavalryman's pronounciation amused me. He spoke gracefully, with a good deal of affectation, pronouncing his *r's* more or less as the French do, but only cinema actors with us.

To be frank, for a moment I was more embarrassed than he. He was so well dressed, while my uniform was partly in rags and partly patched. It is true that I was an officer in a famous brigade, and he a lancer in a regiment serving in the back areas, attached moreover to army headquarters, which was not very close to the front line. But my appearance was so disreputable that I almost felt as if I were in the presence of someone of higher rank. Little by little, however, I fought and managed to conquer the feeling of inferiority that a man who is filthy feels in the presence of one who is clean. In a very few minutes we were on excellent terms.

I led the way and we went up into the front-line trench. He had no fear, but he was determined to show us that he had none, which is always very dangerous in the line. I kept on saying to him: "Do as I do," "Bend down here," "Touch the ground with your hands here," "Stop here," but he did not bend down, touch the ground, or stop. He wanted to look at everything, through the loopholes and above the parapet. I made endless efforts to persuade him to be more prudent.

We stopped in a traverse, to take advantage of the shade. He said to me:

"I think you infantrymen are too cautious. You can't win the war that way."

It was a peculiarly unfortunate remark. His words

were both insulting to me and an affront to my *esprit de corps.*

"That is because we have only our legs to count on," I retorted. "In a ticklish moment an infantryman might find his knees shaking, and if that happens he can't move a step forward. But you are more fortunate. You may be dying of fear, but the legs of your horses will carry you all the same."

I did not repent of having spoken like this until later; for the moment I was satisfied, thinking that the cavalryman had been well answered. He made no reply. We had now reached loophole No. 14.

"This," I explained to him, "is the best loophole in our sector, but it can only be used at night, when the Austrians are sending up rockets. During the day it's forbidden to look through it. The enemy have got it covered with a fixed rifle, and there's always someone there to fire it. Several of our officers and men have been killed or wounded in that way. The men amuse themselves by holding up bits of wood or paper, or coins attached to a small stick, and the bullets never miss the loophole and always strike home on the target."

We both examined the aperture. It was no longer merely a hole made in the wall of the trench and closed with a stone. The men had fixed up an armoured loophole, which had been found in the ruins of Asiago. It was a heavy steel plate, with an opening for observation, which could be closed with a shutter, also made of steel. Keeping under cover, I raised the shutter and waited for the bullet. But the enemy did not fire.

"The sentry's asleep," said my lieutenant.

I let the shutter fall back into its place and then opened it once more. The sun shone through the aperture as if through a lense. There was a whistling sound, accompanied by the sound of a rifle. The ball had passed through the opening.

My cavalry friend thought he would try this himself. He lifted the shutter and held the end of his whip in the opening. Another shot was heard and the whip was broken. He took a piece of wood, fixed a coin to it, and repeated the experiment, saying that he would have something to talk about at army headquarters that night. The coin, struck in the centre, flew off the piece of wood, with a whistling sound. I went on up the trench to show him the next loophole.

"From this one," I explained, "you can see another section of the line, which is of less importance. There's no danger here. Over there you can see a heap that looks like a sack of coal. It's used to mask a machine-gun emplacement. We spotted it a few nights ago, when it was firing after an alarm. We've already informed the regimental commander so that, if there is an attack, it can be knocked out with a mountain gun."

"So you've got some guns?"

"A few are beginning to reach us. Look over there, more to the left. What seems like a white spot is really a loophole commanding the other sector. And there, by that thick patch of fir trees, is a deep ravine. The line is not continuous after that, but begins again on the other side of the ravine."

I thought he was behind me, looking at what I was pointing out. The loophole was a large one and there was room for two in front of it. Then I heard his voice, speaking from a little distance away.

"The knees of an officer of the Royal Piedmont regiment," he was saying, "are steadier than those of his horse." A rifle-shot followed his words. I turned to find my cavalry officer stretched on the ground by loophole 14. I hurried over to him, but he was already dead. A bullet had struck him in the forehead.

Chapter 17

ABOUT THE MIDDLE OF AUGUST THERE WAS MORE TALK of an attack. Our brigade had been reorganized, and a few batteries of field guns and mountain guns had already taken up positions in the sector occupied by our Army Corps. In the line no one now slept at night. Patrols were sent out once more with high-explosive charges. One day we were told that an attack was planned for the following day, but it was postponed, so it was therefore possible to count on at least one more day of life. Those who have not seen active service as we saw it cannot conceive what a joy that was. Even a single hour that could be counted on was much to be thankful for. To be able to say, towards dawn, an hour before the attack: "Well, I can still sleep for another half-hour, and then I shall wake up and smoke a cigarette, boil a cup of coffee and drink it, sip by sip, and smoke another cigarette," would seem almost equivalent to planning out a whole lifetime of pleasant occupation.

Orders to make ready for fresh operations arrived

at the same time as the news that the colours belonging to the two regiments of our brigade had been decorated with gold medals for valour. We should have better appreciated this exceptional honour, which once again singled us out from among all the infantry brigades in the army, had we been out of the line at the time. The brigade commander, however, wished to celebrate the event all the same, and assembled all the officers. In a short speech he recalled the past deeds of the brigade and instructed every company commander to remind his men of them.

I was present, with the other officers of my battalion. After the assembly, which had taken place at brigade headquarters, we walked back to the front line. Behind us were the officers of the first battalion, which was now commanded by Captain Zavattari. He had been transferred to it from the 2nd battalion after the major's death. At this time my battalion was in the trenches and the 1st was in support. To get back to the front line we had to pass the headquarters of the 1st battalion.

We had just arrived there when a report came in that General Leone had been killed, having been hit in the chest by an explosive bullet. It must be confessed that we were all jubiliant at the news. Captain Zavattari invited us to stop at his headquarters and had some bottles of wine opened for us. Glass in hand, he addressed us as follows:

"Gentlemen, I think it may be permitted to a representative of the Ministry of Public Education and a senior captain to raise his glass and drink good fortune to our army. Emulating the fine tradition of certain virile peoples among whom it is customary for the relations to celebrate the death of a member of their family with banquets and with dancing, we—not being in a position to do more—drink to the memory of our general. No occasion this for tears, gentlemen, but for joy, kept of course within suitable bounds. The hand of God has been seen upon the Asiago plateau, and, without complaining of the delay with which Providence manifests the divine will, we may perhaps agree that it was high time. He has left us. Peace be with him! Peace with him, and joy among us. And may we, now that he is dead, at last respect a general whom we detested while he was alive."

We were all standing there with our glasses raised when, on the path coming from Croce de Sant' Antonio, from among the fir trees, there appeared a mounted officer. I was facing the path and was the first to see him. He was coming straight towards us.

"I can't believe it!" I exclaimed.

Everyone looked round. It was General Leone Mounted on a mule, his trench helmet pressed firmly over his eyes, an alpenstock lashed to his saddle, and his field-glasses hanging round his neck, he came trotting towards us, with a sombre look on his face.

"Gentlemen, attention!" cried out Captain Zavattari. We stood at attention, without even having had time to put down our glasses. Captain Zavattari, too, was standing stiffly with his glass in his hand.

"What happy event are you celebrating?" asked the divisional commander in a surly tone.

There was general embarrassment. Zavattari pulled himself together and replied in a voice that seemed to come from beyond the tomb:

"The gold medals which have been awarded to our colours."

"Let me join in your toast," said the general.

Zavattari offered him his own glass, which had not been touched. The general emptied it at a gulp, gave it back to him, and then, putting spurs to his mule, trotted quickly away.

The following day there was an attack, with artillery support. After two batteries had blow holes in the barbed-wire entanglements and destroyed a section of enemy trench, the two companies of the 1st battalion succeeded in entering it. A hundred prisoners fell into our hands, but the trench we had occupied, being exposed to enemy fire from the flank, had subsequently to be evacuated. It was only at this point of the front that the attack was even partially successful.

My own battalion was in reserve, but I took part in the operation carried out by the 2nd battalion, which attacked much farther to the left, beneath the rocky cliffs of Casara Zebio. The divisional commander had decided that at this point artillery should not be used, and that a surprise attack must once more be attempted. In any case two batteries were not enough for the front of an entire division, so that they had to be dispensed with. The general had still not lost his faith in the Farina cuirasses. He thought that an armoured infantry company, advancing *en masse,* would constitute an avalanche of steel against which the enemy's fire would prove unavailing. Lieutenant-Colonel Carriera was the only officer who took up the idea with enthusiasm, and his battalion was chosen to put it into practice.

I was in a front-line trench, watching, at the side of the officer commanding the 2nd battalion. The 6th company, under the orders of Lieutenant Fiorelli, put on their cuirasses. This company was to lead the attack, and the other companies were to follow. Fiorelli, who was also wearing his cuirass, was the first to leave our trenches, and his company followed him. The operation lasted a few minutes only. Enemy machine-guns, posted on the top of the rocks, at once engaged the company and destroyed it, before they had been able to do more than advance a few paces beyond our trenches. The bodies of the men lay in front of us, with their cuirasses shattered as though by the fire of mountain artillery. The colonel had to call the attack off.

The distance between our trenches and the rocks

opposite was not less than two hundred yards at this point. Taking advantage of what cover was offered by the bushes, our men tried to get the wounded in, and while the colonel was watching the first of them being passed into the trench, he showed himself in the breach made for launching the attack and was shot in the arm.

The colonel gave a cry and fell unconscious. His wound did not appear to be grave, but the ball had passed right through his arm. He was tall and fat, and lying stretched out on the ground, he blocked the whole trench and seemed bigger than ever. His face was of a corpse-like pallor, so that for a moment it might almost have been thought that he was dead. The men crowded round him and brought him to by sprinkling brandy on him. Breathing heavily and grinding his teeth, he muttered a few words without opening his eyes. His adjutant, the teacher of Greek, held a brandy flask to his lips and he noisily gulped down all its contents.

The wounded men were still being brought into the trench.

The colonel, supported by two men and with his back against the parapet, was just able to sit up while a stretcher-bearer bandaged his arm. Without opening his eyes he inquired, in a shaky voice:

"What is the time?"

"Ten o'clock," the adjutant replied.

"What time was it when I was wounded?"

"About a quarter to ten."

The captain commanding the 5th company, who was the senior in the battalion, asked if he should take over the command of the battalion.

"No," replied the colonel, his eyes still closed, "I am still in command of the battalion."

He asked how the attack was progressing, and gave several orders. Lieutenant Fiorelli himself had now been brought into the trench. There was a large hole in his cuirass near the shoulder. When, with some difficulty, he had been freed from all that useless steel, it was possible to bandage his wound. His shoulder and collar-bone had been smashed.

Every now and then the colonel asked what time it was. When it was a quarter past ten he sent for the adjutant and, still with closed eyes, made him take down a report, which he dictated more or less as follows:

Headquarters of the 2nd Battalion, 399th Infantry Regiment.

To the officer in command of the 399th Infantry Regiment:

The undersigned, Lieutenant-Colonel Michele Carriera, commanding the 2nd Battalion, 399th Infantry Regiment, has the honour to bring to your notice the conduct of Lieut.-Col. Michele Carriera during the action of August 17, 1916. Gravely wounded in the arm, while leading his battalion to the assault, he refused, in spite of much loss of blood and though in great pain, to give up the command of the battalion or to permit himself to be taken to a dressing-station. Disregarding the danger, he insisted, with stoical resolution, on remaining with his men, and continued to direct the operations, taking all necessary measures. Only half an hour later, when he had assured himself that the attack was continuing according to plan, and after giving the necessary orders to his successor, did he hand over the command and leave the battalion.

For his conduct on this occasion, which comes within the scope of the Royal Decree of 1848, the undersigned has the honour to put forward the name of Lieutenant-Colonel Michele Carricra for the silver military medal for valour. To his subordinates he gave a splendid example of courage and self-sacrifice, etc., etc.

Lieutenant-Colonel in command of the 2nd Battalion.

It was only at this moment that he opened his eyes, took the pen, and signed his name: "Michele Carriera." Then he shut them again.

The captain in command of the 5th company thereupon took command of the battalion, and the stretcher-bearers carried off the colonel on a stretcher. The teacher of Greek was left standing with the paper and pen in his hand, much taken aback. After a moment's thought, anxious that all should be done in due form, he said:

"I've forgotten the date."

He then added: "Casara Zebio, August 17, 1916," to the report.

While these strange bureaucratic operations were going forward, the trench was becoming choked with wounded. The Austrians continued to fire all along the line, for the action was still going on in the rest of the sector. The colonel had hardly been taken away when the deputy surgeon arrived, having been sent by the regimental surgeon to give what first aid he could in the front line. He was a medical student from the University of Naples, and had not yet qualified. The din of battle terrified him. He noticed a cuirass which was lying abandoned on the parapet and, not knowing what had happened to these things in practice, he tried to put it on. Someone showed him others, still being worn by wounded men, which had been punctured as easily as cotton shirts. From that moment, his mission forgotten, he seemed as though dazed, and, with a lost look in his eyes, he continued his way along the trench, bent double although the trench was higher than he was. As he went he stumbled over the wounded men.

"Look out for those men," one of the officers of the battalion called out angrily, "and do something for them."

The deputy surgeon looked at them with a despairing smile. Incapable of keeping upright, he dropped to his hands and knees and crept along on all fours.

"They're attacking!" The cry came from the extreme left of our trench.

There was disorder and confusion. The men at once manned the loopholes, and our machine-guns, which up to then had not been in action, opened fire. I, too, posted myself at a loophole and saw an Austrian column which, having climbed down the mountainside at the end of the ravine, beyond the rock face, was attacking the extreme flank of our trench. Held up by the sudden fire, they themselves started firing from among the rocks.

When everything was quiet again, we looked for the deputy surgeon, but he was nowhere to be found.

Half an hour later, when I rejoined my battalion, I went along to the dressing-station to which Lieutenant Fiorelli had been taken. I had met him at Padua, where he was studying engineering, and I wanted to see if his wound was serious. While I was walking along an approach trench, I heard the cheerful sound of singing, to the accompaniment of a mandolin, issuing from a dugout. I stopped in surprise. Who could be singing so gaily, on the day of an attack, among dead and wounded men? I knew that the dugout was a medical store, and I went up to it and lifted the flap with which the entrance was closed. The place was lit by a candle, and by it, sitting all alone on a case of medicines, was the deputy surgeon, singing and playing the mandolin, with two bottles of liqueur, one empty and the other half full, by his side.

> *"A window looks on a calm blue sea,*
> *A calm blue sea . . . a calm blue sea. . . ."*

I went in. The deputy surgeon stopped singing and let the mandolin fall from his hand. He stared at me in amazement, as though he had seen a ghost.

There was not much difference in rank between us, but I spoke to him formally in order to stress the distance and my anger.

"Aren't you ashamed of yourself, deputy surgeon? Oughtn't you to be on duty?"

He sprang to attention, with head bowed because it was touching the ceiling, but did not answer.

"Is it you," I shouted, "who has emptied those two bottles?"

In a shaky voice and with an air of supplication, he replied:

"Yes, Your Excellency." [1]

---

[1] A title reserved for generals of Army Corps, etc.—*Translator*.

Chapter 18

DURING THE QUIET DAYS THAT FOLLOWED, RUMOURS circulated in the brigade that we really were going to be sent down the line into rest billets at last. In any case we talked of nothing else among ourselves. General Leone came to hear of it and replied with a divisional order which ended thus: "All officers and men must understand that until the war has been won, the only rest permitted is in death." No one talked about rest billets any more.

Although it had no repercussions on the history of the war, I must, for the better comprehension of what follows, put it on record that I was now promoted to command of a company. I took over the 10th, in which I had served since the beginning of the war and which I had commanded on the Carso.

On the same day, as if to celebrate my promotion, the Austrians brought up a trench mortar and fired a few rounds at the trench that was held by my company. From the evidence supplied by an unexploded shell we discovered that it was a mortar with a calibre

155

of 37 mm. Only a few shells were fired at a time, first at one loophole and then at another, and we had two sentries wounded. In spite of all our efforts to spot its position, we failed to discover whether it was located in the trench or some way behind it.

Every day, at different times, and without warning, this mortar fired on us. The divisional commander heard of it and asked for an explanation. The brigade commander passed on all the information he had, but General Leone was not satisfied and came up to the line to see for himself.

When he arrived, I was in the trench. My company was holding the left sector of the battalion front, extending to within a few paces of loophole No. 14, which was situated at the highest point. Farther to the right, and immediately beyond it, was Lieutenant Ottolenghi's machine-gun section, with its two guns, which was attached to us. He was responsible for the extreme right flank of the sector.

General Leone did not call at battalion headquarters, but came straight to the trenches. I saw him and went to meet him. He at once asked me about the trench mortar, and I told him all I knew. When I had finished my report, he overwhelmed me with questions, so that I was again amazed at his interest in details and his wish for mathematical accuracy on the most insignificant points. He wanted to examine, one by one, about fifty loopholes, and he stayed in the sector held by my company for not less than an hour.

"Your loopholes," he informed me at last, "are sighted downwards like the holes in the tower of the Palazzo della Signoria. They seem to have been made for catching grasshoppers instead of observing the enemy trenches."

I took care not to smile, for he had spoken with his grimmest expression. Nevertheless I explained to him why the loopholes in my sector had had to be made differently from those elsewhere, the reason being the lie of the ground, and the position of the trees and rocks on our front.

"It is not the fault of those who made them," I said, "but of the nature of the ground. Look at this loophole, sir. If we were to move the field of fire farther to the left, we should come up against those fir trees and be able to see nothing. If we move it to the right, we are blocked by that rock. And we can't raise it, because those bushes would screen us."

The general patiently examined everything. Every now and then he looked through his field-glasses.

"You're right," he said at last. "The loopholes couldn't have been constructed just as we should have liked. But how am I going to find out the position of that accursed trench mortar? I want to silence it by artillery fire."

The general had become reasonable and moderate. By the time we had arrived at the last loophole in my sector, he had even become polite.

"We first met at Monte Fior, I think."

"Yes, sir."

"You're lucky. You've not been killed yet."

"No, sir."

To my great surprise, he took out his cigarette-case and offered me a cigarette. But he didn't light his, so that I could not very well light mine.

When we reached the end of my company's sector, I said to him:

"This is where my sector ends, and the next belongs to the machine-gun section. Would you like me to go any farther with you, sir?"

"Yes, please. If you will be so good."

He could not have been more affable. I was delighted; he seemed a different person.. We had now entered the sector belonging to the machine-gun section and I was walking in front of him, leading the way. Lieutenant Ottolenghi, who had probably been warned, came towards us. I pointed him out to the general, explaining that he was the officer in charge of the sector, and stood back, leaving them face to face.

"Show me what loopholes you have," said the general to Ottolenghi. "I suppose you know them. Have you been in this sector long?"

"More than a week, sir. I have readjusted all the loopholes myself, so I'm familiar with all of them.

Ottolenghi led the way, the general followed, and I brought up the rear; behind us were the two *carabinieri* whom the general had brought with him when he came into the line, and my orderly. All was quiet in the trench. During the whole of the general's inspection the trench mortar had given no sign of life, though sometimes from the enemy lines came a single rifle-shot, to which our sentries replied.

Ottolenghi stopped between two loopholes, which he explained were subsidiary ones, and said:

"These loopholes only command our own wire and were not made for observing the enemy's trenches."

The general looked at both of them carefully.

"These are of no use either for observation or for fire. You'll kindly have them destroyed and have others made. Where are the chief loopholes?"

The general had once more become authoritative.

"Here, a little farther on, is the best loophole in the sector," replied Ottolenghi. "All the ground in front can be observed from it as well as the whole of the enemy line. I don't think a better loophole exists than No. 14."

"Let me have a look at it," said the general.

"Loophole No. 14!" I said to myself. As I had not been in the sector for several days, I concluded that Ottolenghi had abolished that loophole, changed the number, and given it to another.

Ottolenghi stopped at the first bend in the trench. There was no alteration in the loopholes; they were just the same as before. There, standing apart, on the far side of the bend, higher than the rest and more conspicuous, was loophole No. 14 with its steel shutter. Ottolenghi stopped on the farther side of it, leaving it between himself and the general.

"Here it is," he said to the general, lifting the shutter and suddenly letting it fall again. "The aperture is small and only one person can look through it at a time."

I struck some stones with my stick, to attract Ottolenghi's attention. I tried to catch his eye in order to sign to him to stop this; but he wouldn't look at me. He understood me well enough, though he would not meet my eye. His face was pale and my own heart seemed almost to have stopped beating. I instinctively opened my mouth in order to call the general back, but no sound came. Possibly my agitation prevented me from speaking. I do not want, in any way, to underestimate my responsibility at that moment. The general was in danger of being shot. I could have prevented it, and I did not say a word.

The general planted himself in front of the loophole, close to the steel shield, bending his head until he almost touched it, and then lifted the shutter and put his eye to the aperture. I shut my eyes.

I cannot say how long I waited. But I heard no shot. Then the general said:

"It's splendid. Splendid!"

I opened my eyes and saw that he was still at the loophole. Without moving away from it, he went on:

"It looks to me now—as if that mortar were in the trench. Still, it's not easy to say. . . . It might be—

where the line of the trench is broken—but I'm not
sure. What a good view this gives! An excellent loophole. Of course the mortar may be mounted a few
paces behind the trench—in the wood."

Ottolenghi proceeded to prompt him.

"Look to the left, sir. Can you see a white sand-
bag?"

"Yes, easily. I can see everything."

"I think the mortar's over there. There's nothing
to be seen, no smoke or anything, but the noise comes
from that direction. Can you see, sir?"

"Yes, yes."

"Don't move, sir. Have a good look at it."

"It's possible you're right."

"If you'll permit it, sir, we could open fire. I could
bring a machine-gun into action. They might then
open fire with the mortar as a counter-measure."

"Very well. Do as you say."

The general stepped back from the loophole and
let the shutter fall. Ottolenghi ordered a machine-
gun to open fire, and the general then returned to the
loophole and once more lifted the shutter.

The mortar did not fire. There were merely a few
single shots from the enemy trench. The general took
his head away from the loophole two or three times
in order to speak to Ottolenghi, and the sunlight then
shone through the aperture. While the machine-gun
was firing, the general observed the result first with

the left eye and then with the right.

The sound of isolated shots and the tapping of the machine-gun did not wake the sniper with the fixed rifle. The general left the loophole. Ottolenghi was much upset.

"I'll have some bombs thrown," he said to the general. "And then you can have another look, sir."

"No," replied the general, "that's enough for to-day. But I congratulate you. Tomorrow I'll bring my Chief of Staff here so that he can have a good look at the enemy positions. Good day."

He shook hands with each of us and, followed by the two carabineers, went off, leaving us alone together.

"You're mad," I said to Ottolenghi.

My orderly was only a few paces away, but he appeared oblivious of us both. Ottolenghi made no reply. He was red in the face and seemed unable to stand still for one moment.

"Shall we see whether that fool of a sniper will wake up if we open the shutter again?"

He took a small coin out of his pocket, held it lightly between his thumb and first finger, and, opening the shutter, placed it in the aperture, through which the sun was still shining. The whine of a bullet and the sound of a shot reached us at the same moment, and the coin went spinning away into the fir trees.

Ottolenghi, beside himself with rage, was stamping

about, biting his fingers and swearing as I had never heard him swear before.

"And now," he sputtered, "now he's going to send us the Chief of Staff!"

That night we dismantled loophole No. 14.

Chapter 19

THERE WAS NO TALK OF FURTHER ATTACKS. QUIET seemed to have descended indefinitely upon the valley. On both sides positions were being strengthened; the engineers were working all night. The 37-mm. trench mortar continued to annoy us, but still remained invisible. For days on end it did not fire a shot and then, without warning, it would bombard a loophole and wound one of our sentries.

My battalion was still in the line and we were waiting to be relieved by the battalion in reserve. Wishing to provide definite information about the mortar for the company commander who would take over from me, I had organized a special watch night and day in the hope that the flash of the discharge or the movements of the gun crew would betray the position of the piece. But as this watch had produced no result, I decided, on the night before we were relieved, to go and see what I could find out for myself, and I ordered a corporal to accompany me on a patrol. This man had often been out on patrol before and knew the ground well. The moon lit up the forest, and from time to time the light of an occasional rocket flashed through the branches, giving as it did so an effect of movement to the tree-trunks. It was difficult to tell whether this was always an illusion or not, for the moving shadows might well have been men.

The two of us had crawled out from the extreme left of the company's front, at a point where our trenches were nearest to those of the Austrians. Working our way along on all fours, we had reached a bush about ten paces in front of our line and about thirty from the enemy's. A slight depression lay between our trench and this bush, which was growing on a rise that dominated the trench opposite it.

As we waited, without moving, uncertain whether to go on or to stop where we were, it seemed to us that we could detect some movement in the enemy trenches to our left. At that point there were no trees, so it could not have been an optical illusion. In any case, we soon realized that we were in a position that enabled us to see along the enemy trench. We had never so far discovered any point from which this was possible, and I therefore decided to stay there all night, in order to watch what was going on among the enemy as soon as dawn began to break. Whether the mortar fired or not was no longer a matter of interest to me. The important thing was to stay at this unexpectedly favourable vantage-point.

The ridge, with its low-growing bush, afforded

such excellent protection that I decided to connect it with our line and make a permanent clandestine lookout. I sent the corporal back to fetch a sergeant of engineers, to whom I explained the work I wanted done. In a few hours a communication trench had been made between our line and the bush. The sound of digging was covered by firing from our line. The trench was not deep, but sufficiently so to protect a man crawling along it, even by day. The earth that had been excavated was carried into the trench, so that no visible traces of what had been done remained; small green branches and bushes completed the work of concealment.

The corporal and I stayed beneath that bush all night, without being able to see any signs of life in the enemy trench. But at daybreak our long vigil was rewarded. To begin with, there was a confused coming and going of shadowy figures, and then men appeared in the trench carrying camp kettles. It was a fatigue party with coffee. They passed, in ones and twos, without bending down, certain that they could not be seen, for the trench and its traverses protected them from both observation and enfilading fire from our lines. I had never seen anything like it before. There they were, those Austrians—so close that we could almost touch them, and as quiet and unperturbed as pedestrians on a city pavement. It gave me an extraordinary sensation. I clutched the arm of the corporal, who was on my right, to communicate to him, without speaking, my amazement. He, too, was watching intently, and I could feel the tremor that ran through his body as a result of holding his breath for so long. An unknown existence had suddenly revealed itself to us. Those strongly defended trenches, which we had attacked so many times without success, had ended by seeming to us inanimate, like desolate buildings, uninhabited by men, the refuge only of mysterious and terrible beings of whom we knew nothing. Now they were showing themselves to us as they really were, men and soldiers like us, in uniform like us, moving about, talking, and drinking coffee, just as our own comrades behind us were doing at that moment. It seemed so very strange. Somehow I had never thought of them like that. They were actually having coffee! And why shouldn't they have coffee? Why should their having coffee appear strange to me? No doubt between ten and eleven they were going to eat their rations, just as we were. Obviously the enemy could not live without eating and drinking. Then what was the cause of my bewilderment?

They were all so close to us that we could count them, one by one. There was a small circular space in their trench, between two traverses, in which from time to time one or two of them stepped, evidently to speak to one another, though we could not hear their voices. This circular space appeared to be in front of a dugout larger than the others, because there was more coming and going at that point. But all movement ceased as an officer suddenly appeared. It was clear that he was an officer from the way in which he was dressed. His belt and leggings were of yellow leather, and his uniform looked brand-new. He had probably just arrived at the front, no doubt from some military school. He was very young, and his fair hair made him appear younger still. In fact he looked scarcely eighteen. As soon as he arrived the soldiers disappeared and no one else remained in the circular space. Coffee was apparently just being served out. I could see no one but this young officer.

I had been at the front ever since the beginning of the war. Campaigning for years on end means that one acquires military habits and outlook. Big-game hunting for men is not so different from other kinds of big-game hunting. It was not a man that I was looking at, but an enemy. After so much waiting, so many patrols, so much lost sleep, I had my quarry over my sights. The hunt had been successful. Mechanically, without a thought, without any special desire, but as it were instinctively, I held out my hand for the corporal's rifle. He gave it to me. If as on other nights we had been lying on the ground, it is probable that I should have fired at once, without losing a second. But I was kneeling, in a trench, and the bush was in front of me, masking me from an aimed shot. I was under good cover and could take my time before I fired. Planting my elbows firmly on the ground, I proceeded to take aim.

The Austrian officer lit a cigarette. Now he was smoking. This cigarette formed an invisible link between us. No sooner did I see its smoke than I wanted a cigarette myself; which reminded me that I had some with me. All this took place in a moment; but the act of aiming, which had been automatic, became rational. I was forced to remember that I was taking aim, and that I was aiming at somebody. The finger that was on the trigger slackened its pressure. I began to think. I found I was forced to think.

There was no doubt that I considered the war morally and politically justified. My conscience as a man and a citizen was not in conflict with my military duties. War was, for me, a hard necessity, terrible, to be sure, but one to which I submitted, as one of the many necessities, unpleasant but inevitable, of life. Moreover, I was on campaign and there were men fighting under my orders. That is to say, morally, I was fighting twice over. I had already taken part in many engagements. It was therefore quite logical for me to fire on an enemy officer. I insisted on my men keeping alert while on patrol, and shooting straight if the enemy offered them a target. Then why did I not fire on this officer? I knew it was my duty to fire. Otherwise it would have been monstrous for me to have continued to fight and to make others do so. There was no doubt about it: I ought to fire.

And yet I did not. My mind was working clearly, and my nerves were quite calm. The previous evening, before leaving our front line, I had slept for four or five hours, and I felt perfectly fit as I lay in the trench behind the bush, nor was I in any kind of danger. I could not have felt less excited if I had been sitting in my own room at home.

Perhaps it was that very lack of excitement that turned my thoughts away from the war. In front of me I had a young officer who was quite unconscious of the danger that threatened him. I could not have missed him. I could have fired a thousand rounds at that range and never have missed once. All I had to do was to press the trigger and he would have fallen dead. The certainty that his life depended solely on my will made me hesitate. What I had in front of me was a man. A man!

I could see his face perfectly clearly. The light was increasing and the sun was just becoming visible behind the tops of the mountains. Could I fire like this, at a few paces, on a man—as if he were a wild boar?

I began to think that perhaps I ought not to do so. I reasoned like this: To lead a hundred, even a thousand, men against another hundred, or thousand, was one thing; but to detach one man from the rest and say to him, as it were: "Don't move, I'm going to shoot you. I'm going to kill you"—that was different. Entirely different. To fight is one thing, but to kill a man is another. And to kill him like that is to murder him.

I don't know to what extent my thoughts were logical, but I do know that I put down the rifle and I did not fire. I felt two consciences, almost two personalities, within me, in conflict with each other. "You can't kill a man like that!" I said to myself. Although I myself lived through those moments, I am not able now to reconstruct my psychological state at the time. There was a break in my logic which today I can no longer clearly recall, for I still ask myself how, having arrived at this conclusion, I could think of letting another do what I could not reconcile with my own conscience. I had the rifle with its barrel through the branches of the bush, and the butt resting on the ground. The corporal was close beside me. Signing to him to take the butt, I whispered: "Look here—I'm not going to fire on a man, alone, like that. Will you?"

The corporal took hold of the rifle-butt. Then he said:

"No, I won't either."

We crept back into our trenches, on all fours. Coffee had already been served out and we had ours too.

That evening, as soon as it was dark, we were relieved by the reserve battalion.

Chapter 20

IT SEEMED AS IF THE HIGHER COMMAND HAD PUT A stop to operations. They were continuing on other fronts, particularly on the Carso; but the plateau was quiet once more. In the middle of September the brigade was sent to rest billets for a fortnight in the neighbourhood of Foza. We at last received fresh uniforms and clothing and were reoutfitted. But for the most part we did nothing but sleep.

In October, with the approach of winter, which begins early in the mountains, our spells in the trenches, grim and monotonous, started once more. But in spite of everything they were not really worse than the kind of everyday life which, in normal times, is lived by millions of miners in the large coal-bearing areas in Europe. We had an occasional casualty, but rarely a fatal one. Now and then a shell from a big gun or a trench mortar would cause something of a catastrophe, just as serious accidents sometimes happen in the mines. But life went on just the same: a spell in the trenches, then a few days in support, a kilometre down the line, and then the trenches again. Cold, snow, ice, and avalanches did not make war any worse for men who were fit. They were familiar things to all who, in peace-time, lived in the mountains or in regions of eternal snows. For infantry, war means attacks. If there are no attacks, there is no war, only hard work.

That is why today I can recall nothing whatever of many of those weeks which so closely resembled one another. I shall therefore have to pass over whole months and stop only at certain incidents, some of which lasted a few minutes only, but which made so deep an impression on me that even now they stand out vividly in every detail among my memories.

General Leone, who had been promoted to a higher command, left the division. We celebrated that for a wcck. His successor, General Piccolomini, arrived while the brigade was in the trenches. Wishing to get into touch with his men at once, he came to visit us in the line.

My company was holding the same trenches as before, on the left flank of the sector. A runner sent by the battalion commander warned me of the general's arrival, and I went to meet him. General Leone had been a grim and rigid-looking man; the new general had a cheerful air and was quick in his movements. In comparison with the former he seemed to me, at first sight, a very good fellow.

I don't remember where he came from. Perhaps he

had been in command of some military college, for he had a pedagogic mind, much given to theory. I was expecting questions about my men, and their morale, about the trenches, and about the enemy. But, with the air of an examiner, he said:

"Let me see, young man. How would you define victory? I mean our victory, victory by force of arms."

I had not expected such a question. I tried to assume an intelligent expression, with that special smile that people assume when, not having in the least understood what they have been asked, but finding it inopportune to say so, they wish to convey to their questioner that they have understood moderately well, but, in effect, so very moderately that it is much the same as if they had not understood at all.

The general repeated his words.

"We were speaking of victory. Do I make myself clear? Are we fighting to win, or to lose? Obviously to win!"

"Yes, sir, of course!"

"Exactly. To win the war is to be victorious. I should like you to define that victory."

By now I had understood only too well. And I thought, not exactly with longing, but with less horror than before, of General Leone, who in recent times had not come near us at all and had almost appeared to have recovered his senses.

The general insisted on my replying, and I had to make up my mind to do so.

"I hardly know, sir," I said. "Paolo, the legal authority, maintains—that all definitions are dangerous." And modestly, even with a certain shyness, I plucked up courage to cap this quotation with a Latin tag, one of the few that had remained to me from the time when I was a student of law.

Confronted by my Latin, the general seemed somewhat taken aback. He had not expected Latin. If I was nonplussed over the definition of victory, so was he over Paolo. However, he pulled himself together and spoke with decision.

"I'm not a priest and have never been in a seminary. In consequence I know no Latin."

I thought it more prudent to hold my tongue.

"We can leave San Paolo out of it. But your definition of victory, what is it?" the general insisted.

Seeing, with satisfaction, that I was not in a position to provide it, he hastened to come to my aid, and defined victory in words which, taken probably from some military text-book, I now no longer remember, except that they included something about "nervous energy." The general proceeded to distinguish between a victorious offensive and a victorious defensive. In the first case the "nervous energy" was released, at the right moment, and, in the second, restrained.

"Let us hope," I thought, "that in practice, at least, he will be better than General Leone." The general interrupted my reflections.

"I'll wager that, in the whole of your battalion, there isn't a single officer who knows this important definition."

"I hope not," I thought; but aloud I said:

"It's quite likely, sir."

There was nothing but an occasional rifle-shot to be heard up and down our trench. The general went along it nimbly and confidently, with me leading the way. It was obvious that he had none of that preoccupation with personal safety which is common to all who are unaccustomed to life in the trenches. But his thoughts were evidently still fixed on the theory of war. Every time we stopped he said:

"This brigade is used to fighting, but not to thinking. Even officers are without the most elementary ideas."

I did not reply.

"Take care, sir, bend down. This place is under fire."

"Let them fire," he replied contemptuously, and went on, hardly bending at all. A shot soon warned us that it was necessary to be more careful. He halted and said:

"I think I'll reply to those fellows myself."

He stopped a man who was passing on some fatigue and took his rifle from him. Then he went on a few paces till he came to a loophole. It was not one of our best loopholes, having been made simply for keeping watch on a stretch of our wire which the lie of the ground made favourable for the unobserved approach of hostile patrols. The area it commanded was far removed from the enemy trenches, and it was quite impossible to fire at them from it. In fact, it belonged to that category of loopholes which General Leone had designated as "made for catching grasshoppers."

The general had a good look, snapped up his sight, and took careful aim. Then he steadily fired all the six rounds in his clip one after another. The men on fatigue had stopped and were looking on respectfully. The general turned to them.

"I wanted to give a lesson to those ruffians, in person. Tell your comrades that your general is not afraid of handling a rifle like any of his men."

He was visibly pleased with himself, and even rather moved. The men knew very well that the loophole was not one that commanded any hostile trenches. But I did not think it incumbent on me to point out to him that he had been firing into the ground and on our own wire.

I thought our short halt was at an end, when I noticed that the general's attention appeared to be riveted upon the barrel of the rifle he had borrowed. He had noticed that it was without a bayonet, though men in the front line were obliged to keep them fixed.

"Where's the bayonet?" he demanded.

I explained to him that men on fatigue duties never fixed their bayonets, and that the rifle he held belonged to a man on fatigue.

He asked for the bayonet, and the man to whom the rifle belonged hastened to give it to him. The general fixed it himself and gazed intently at the point. The bayonet had been well sharpened, but there was some rust on it, as I perceived at once. "That fool of a sergeant," I said to myself, "has forgotten to inspect bayonets; now we shall have trouble." I waited for the general to reprimand me, as the officer responsible, and tried to think of some plausible excuse. But he paid no attention to me. After having examined the point of the bayonet carefully, he said to the man:

"What can you see here?"

The man himself realized that the bayonet had not been cleaned, and turned red. The general went on:

"What can you see here? You needn't be ashamed. Come closer and have a good look. What's written here? Something *is* written here, you know."

The man approached and looked carefully. Not all the men in the company could read; among the peasants there was, in fact, a high percentage of illiteracy. I fervently hoped that this one at least knew his letters.

He certainly looked as if he could read, because he gazed at the bayonet with an intelligent air, but, after examining it, from the point to the hilt, he answered in confusion:

"I can't see anything, sir."

I had a good look too, but could see nothing. Neither on the blade itself nor on the point was there so much as a single letter. There was nothing whatever but rust.

The general clapped the man on the shoulder and exclaimed:

"Idiot! A word is written here which all can read, even those who have never learned their alphabet; a word which shines out so clearly that even the blind can see it." Turning to me for confirmation, he said: "Isn't that so?"

As I had been unable to see anything myself, I could not very well corroborate his statement. Somewhat embarrassed, I shook my head and half assented, as if to say: "I leave it to you."

The general now turned to the whole of the fatigue party, who were ranged below the parapet, at attention, and addressed them magisterially.

"Victory is written here. Victory! You understand? It's for victory that we are fighting from the Alps to the sea, from the Adriatic to the Tyrrhenian. For victory! Victory in the name of the King! In the name of Italy. In the name of . . ."

The general coughed discreetly.

"In the name of . . ."

As the third invocation failed him, he coughed a second time, and then a third. At last, with a sudden inspiration, he brought things to an end with:

"Long live the King!"

Carried away by his eloquence, the general had raised his voice. The Austrians must have heard it. The trench mortar of 37-mm. calibre, which was still invisible, promptly fired three rounds at our trench. We were in no danger, because we happened to be in a safe place. The trench mortar could not reach us, and there were not even sentries at that point. The general, who could not be expected to know so much, did not move and remained very calm.

"Does it fire often?" he asked without losing his composure.

"Not very often," I replied, by way of reprisal.

"Perhaps they were replying to the shots I fired."

"Possibly, sir."

The general gave back the rifle and the bayonet, and the fatigue party went on. We remained alone together. He grew cautious and took up the conversation again in very low tones.

"Have all your soldiers knives?"

"Not all of them, sir. Some have and some haven't."

"The bayonet's not enough. In a mêlée, especially at night, knives are essential. A knife with a sharp point to it. A sharp point, you understand."

"Oh, yes, sir."

"How many men have knives in your company?"

I had not the remotest idea. As a rule every man had a knife or penknife which was his personal property. But some had neither. Experience, however, had taught me that, in the interests of the service, when confronted with questions of this kind, it was as well to provide statistics. I made a rapid calculation. At that time there were about two hundred men in the company.

"A hundred and fifty," I answered.

"With fixed handles?"

"No, sir. I've not seen any of that sort."

"You don't inspect these knives very often?"

"No, sir. As they belong to the men, I didn't think it necessary."

"You'll do so from now on."

"Very good, sir."

"Do your men use their knives often?"

"Yes, sir."

The general lowered his voice still more, came closer to me, and, almost whispering in my ear, demanded:

"For what purpose?"

I replied in the same tone of voice.

"For cutting bread . . ."

The general stared at me. I could not stop myself, and went on:

"And meat—and cheese . . ."

The general seemed to be devouring me with his eyes. I continued:

"And for peeling oranges."

"No, no," he exclaimed with a horrified air. "I mean in action."

I thought this over for a moment, all the more because the low voice in which I was addressed seemed to induce meditation. In action! We had not succeeded in doing much damage to the Austrians with rifles, let alone knives! Instead of answering I repeated in scarcely audible tones:

"In action?"

The general's thoughts were running on. He did not notice that I had not replied to his question. He continued:

"It's obvious that a rifle with fixed bayonet must be grasped by both hands. In order to be free to do this, the knife should be held between the teeth."

He suited the action to the word by putting his first finger between his teeth. The strange attitude he took up and the look he gave me at the same time, with the ends of his moustache protruding from his lip, made me think of an otter with a fish in its mouth. I nodded to show him that I understood.

"The stroke must be rapid. It doesn't matter whether at the heart or the throat, so long as it's done smartly."

Again I nodded. It was obvious that the less I said, the better things were likely to go.

"It's best to have a single type of knife with a fixed handle. You understand?"

"Yes, sir."

"Mention it to your battalion commander."

"Very good, sir."

The general shook hands with me. The gesture seemed almost cabbalistic, as if between us some mysterious pact had been concluded.

Some days later General Piccolomini wished the brigade commander to present the officers of both regiments to him. All company commanders and other officers who were not on duty were present at the assembly. He wanted to get to know us all, and he made use of the occasion to deliver an open-air lecture to us. This took place in the area belonging to the reserve battalion in the brigade. The divisional order of the day had already made public the subject of the lecture, which was to be on the Co-ordination of Intellects. The weather was splendid, and the plateau had never looked more lovely.

After welcoming the officers of the brigade in a few sentences, the general got on to his subject. The expression "co-ordination of intellects" recurred time after time. Co-ordination of the intellect of the commanding officer with those of his subordinates; co-ordination of the intellect of the infantryman with that of the gunner; co-ordination of the intellect of the officers with those of the men, and so forth and so on. The general was able to bring in a number of definitions, which he knew by heart. I heard once again that of victory as related to nervous energy. But the intellect itself was the core of the discourse. The general spoke without notes and became almost lyrical as he warmed to his subject.

"An unclouded intellect, as clear as the sunlight of this radiant morning—in which an infinite number of atoms are dancing in divine accord, as I should like the officers of my division to do on the day of battle— an intellect that finds the smallest key sufficient to open a large door, a word all that is required to grasp the meaning of an order, and an intuition enough to reveal at the first glance the implications of an unknown fact: that is the kind of intellect needed. For instance—"

The general stopped. He had noticed a semicircular excavation, evidently new, which, masked by branches, crowned the top of a mound about a hundred paces away.

"For instance—what is that excavation? Is it necessary to have constructed it in order to know what it is? Of course not. Nor is it necessary to inquire. It's enough to see it. It explains itself. One knows intuitively that it is a machine-gun emplacement."

The general paused like a conjuror who, having produced a rabbit out of a hat, waits complacently for the enthusiastic applause of his audience.

The adjutant major belonging to the 2nd battalion, the teacher of Greek, was too scrupulous to allow anything to pass without contradiction that was not strictly true. It was his battalion that was in reserve and he knew the sector well. Accuracy before everything.

He took a pace to the front.

"Excuse me, sir," he said.

"Yes?" said the general.

"As a matter of fact, sir, it isn't a machine-gun emplacement."

"Oh. What is it, then?"

"It's a latrine, sir."

It was a bad moment for everyone. The general coughed. One or two of us coughed too. The lecture was at an end.

Chapter 21

BY NOVEMBER THE SNOW WAS ALREADY DEEP. EVERY time there was a fresh fall, we had to bank up the trenches and adjust the loopholes to the new level. There had been a change in the army command, and it was said that operations would soon begin. The engineers were busy constructing portable bridges and scaling-ladders, and we had to carry out exercises with them. The bridges were made with interlaced branches and were intended to be of use in getting over enemy wire. The ladders were of wood, about seven or eight yards long, and were supposed to be used for taking by escalade those enemy trenches which, on the left of the sector, the Austrians had constructed above the rock face. The bridges and ladders were discussed and derided by day and night. The attack was thought to be imminent.

My company was in the line, at the extreme right of that sector in which the distance between our trenches and those of the enemy was greatest. On our right were the big rocks, on our left the narrow ravine, almost bare of trees. On both our right and our left the trenches were closer together, but in the centre the intervening space widened out until the distance separating them was between two and three hundred yards. At this point the Austrian trenches were on high ground and dominated ours, which lay about thirty yards lower down.

The battalion commander had sent Private Marrasi, once again in trouble, up into the line, under fifteen days' arrest, and had assigned him to my company. To get out of trench life, he had pretended that he knew German and he had therefore been sent, in the first instance, to a telephone interception post. When it was discovered that he did not understand a word of the language, he was punished and sent back to his battalion. I had not seen him since the operations on Monte Fior, although he belonged to the 9th company. I attached him to the 2nd platoon, and he started duty at once, because there was no arrest while in the trenches, merely loss of pay.

That night, during a trench inspection, my attention was attracted by a conversation which was taking place in the dugout belonging to the 2nd platoon, which lay twenty or thirty paces behind the trench. I went closer and found the men smoking and chatting in low voices, round the lighted stoves. There was no officer commanding the platoon, and the non-commissioned officer in charge, Sergeant Cosello, was the only man who was taking no part in the conversation. He was sitting with his legs crossed smoking a pipe with a terracotta bowl and a mouthpiece of inordinate length, while he listened to what the others were saying.

"I was born on a Friday," said one of them, "and it was clear I was not going to have much luck. My mother died the same day. The day I was called to the colours was a Friday; the first attack I was in was on a Friday. The first wound I got was on a Friday, and on a Friday I got a second. I know I shall be killed on a Friday. I'll bet you the attack will be fixed for Friday next."

"Well, I was born on Sunday," another man said, "and I haven't had any more luck than you. My mother died too, six months after I was born, which comes to much the same thing. My father had to marry again for my sake, because, with his wages, he couldn't afford a wet nurse. My stepmother beat me as though I were a mattress; that's the first thing I can remember about my childhood. I wouldn't wish a dog to live the life I lived. Later the war broke out. Do you remember what day of the week it was when that hand-grenade burst at my feet?"

"I was there at the time."

"Well, it was a Sunday. You can have my birthday if you want it."

"And when were you born, Marrasi?"

Marrasi did not reply.

"If there is a day in the week that brings luck, you

must have been born on it. How many attacks have you really been in? With one excuse or another, you've got out of every one. That's luck for you!"

Marrasi defended himself by counter-attacking.

"Who'll give me half a cigar?" he asked.

"*Ja!* Half a cigar!"

"*Ja, ja!*"

"*Kamarad,* half a cigar."

They laughed at his German, but would not give him the cigar.

"And that wound in the hand? Clever of you to get that! How did you manage it, eh?"

"But when you were taken prisoner, your luck was out. All gone."

Everyone laughed. The sergeant went on smoking imperturbably.

I forgot about Marrasi. One the following day I was in my dugout making drawings for the battalion commander. It might have been about two o'clock in the afternoon, when there was an alarm on our front, followed by a few shots. The whole line at once opened fire. I rushed into the trench: the men were manning the loopholes. I myself ran to the nearest loophole and looked out. Half-way across the little valley, beyond the line of our wire, I saw Marrasi, without his rifle, and with his hands above his head, staggering knee-deep in the snow towards the enemy trenches. Above the noise of the shots, I heard the stentorian voice of Sergeant Cosello shouting:

"Fire on that deserter!"

The enemy trenches were silent.

I had to hurry off to the telephone, for the battalion commander was asking for an explanation of what was happening. He spoke with agitation.

"What's the matter? Do you want to be reinforced?"

I reassured him.

"No, no. It's only one of our men who's deserting to the enemy; he's alone, without his rifle, and the others are firing on him. The Austrians aren't firing, so as not to frighten him."

"It's a disgrace to the battalion!"

"You needn't tell me that, sir. But what am I to do?"

"Send the man to me, alive or dead."

"It won't be easy to send him alive. The whole company's firing on him."

"Never mind. He's better dead. Send him to me dead."

"Very good, sir. Is that all, sir?"

"Yes. You can go now, but let me know what happens as soon as possible."

I went back to my loophole. The two machine-guns belonging to the battalion had now joined in the firing. Marrasi went on advancing, but only with the greatest difficulty. He was now climbing the opposite side of the valley. The ground rose sharply and the snow was deeper than ever. I was amazed that he had

not yet fallen. Then I became aware that he was being followed, about fifty paces behind, by Sergeant
Cosello, who was also half buried in the snow. Cosello
was grasping his rifle in both hands, and after every
step he fired at Marrasi. But Marrasi did not fall. I
shouted to the sergeant with all my strength to come
back to our trenches. He stopped, in the middle of
the valley. Fearing that the Austrians would fire on
him, I repeated the order. He turned round and
called out:

"Very good, sir."

His legs were buried in snow. Steadying himself,
he took careful aim and emptied a whole clip of cartridges at the deserter. Marrasi fell and rolled over in
the snow. I thought that he had been hit, but in a few
moments he got up again and continued on his way.
The whole line went on firing at him, yet he went on
unhurt. Even the sergeant, who was a very good shot,
had missed him. I have often noticed that in moments of great tension men are apt to fire with both
their eyes open and without taking proper aim at all.

The sergeant got back into the trench and came
over to me, panting and covered with sweat. He spoke
with difficulty.

"What a disgrace!" he kept repeating. "What a
disgrace for the 2nd platoon!"

The 2nd platoon was disgraced; so was the company; so was the battalion. No doubt before long the
whole regiment would feel disgraced—not to speak

of the brigade, the division, the Army Corps, and in all probability the entire army. Meanwhile Marrasi continued on his way.

The telephone operator came running up to tell me that the battalion commander wanted me again, because the regimental commander insisted on being kept informed of what was happening. I replied that I was in the line and could not come for the moment. The operator disappeared. Marrasi was getting farther and farther away. The Austrians had two stretches of wire in front of their trenches, and he had now reached the first. It was almost entirely covered by the snow, but this did not make it any the less difficult to get over. He took hold of some of the strands, shook them, and attempted to climb over them, but all to no purpose. Realizing that he would never be able to get through, he stopped for a moment and in his discouragement pressed his hands to his head. It seemed as though he no longer had the strength to go on. Then he took a few despairing steps at random, turning this way and that as if lost; still under fire from our men, and still invulnerable.

At last he pulled himself together and went with determination towards a tree a few paces away, on our side of the wire. The Austrians had set up a *cheval de frise* against it from the other side. Marrasi took off his belt with the two cartridge-holders, which he was still wearing, and, thus unencumbered, climbed up the trunk with agility. He was soon several yards above ground level. From there he jumped and disappeared into the snow on the other side of the wire. The first obstacle had been surmounted.

Our men continued firing, but the Austrians did not reply.

The telephone operator came back again. The battalion commander, overwhelmed with questions from the regimental commander, who in his turn was being continually pressed for information by the brigade commander, was insisting that I should speak to him over the telephone. I sent the man away, calling after him:

"Put a few shots into the telephone wire, then go and tell the battalion commander the line's been cut."

"Very good, sir."

"You understand?"

"Yes, sir."

Still under the ineffective fusillade and the fire of the machine-guns, Marrasi again went forward. The last stretch was the steepest and the most exhausting. The enemy trench was now only a few paces away. A hand beckoned to him from a large loophole, and he went towards it. Our best marksmen with rifle grenades now seemed to be getting the range. A grenade exploded near him and he fell, but he got up again immediately.

Firing was now going on everywhere in the sector. From the company it had spread to the battalion, then to the battalions on either flank beyond Monte Interrotto and as far as Val d'Assa. Everyone was firing, the Austrians as well as our own men, and it seemed as though a whole army corps were engaged. Only the trench opposite held its fire.

Marrasi was now below the second line of wire, and not more than a couple of paces from the Austrian line. Someone must have been speaking to him in Italian from the large loophole, for he seemed to be answering. Just as he reached the wire, he fell and lay motionless with his legs buried in the snow, his body bent forward and his arms stretched out. The fire of our whole line was still concentrated upon this now inanimate target.

It was some time before I was able to stop the firing in our sector. And when at last it ceased, it still continued in the sectors on either side. The telephone was not working, so that I had to send a written report to the battalion commander. I had difficulty in refusing, until after dark, to carry out the regimental commander's order that a patrol should be sent out, under the command of an officer, to fetch in the body and so wipe out the stain on the honour of the regiment. The colonel eventually came up into the line to see in person that his orders were executed. But even he could not alter the circumstances. The body still lay there, beyond the wire, about three hundred paces from our line, and about two from that of the enemy. It was impossible to retrieve it in broad daylight. The colonel, however, was insistent, and seeing that all other arguments were useless, I took refuge in a literary one. Having just been reading Ariosto, I quoted, in all seriousness, a passage dealing with Cloridano and Medoro:

"Che sarebbe pensier non troppo accorto
Perder dei vivi per salvar un morto." [1]

Whereupon I was severely and summarily reprimanded by the colonel.

But the patrol did not go out, after all.

It grew dark, and the first rocket we fired showed us that the body of Marrasi had disappeared.

The assault we were to undertake with ladders and bridges was postponed.

---

[1] "For it would scarcely be wise to lose men's lives in saving a dead man."

Chapter 22

WITH THE BEGINNING OF WINTER, LEAVE RECOM-
menced. A fortnight at home seemed unexampled
happiness to us. Avellini and I, who were two of the
senior officers in the battalion, were due to go on leave
among the first. But the assault to be undertaken
with ladders and bridges, which had been postponed
so often, was again in preparation, and the colonel
would not let us go. Furthermore, I was trying to get
my leave to coincide with that of my brother, who
was serving in another infantry regiment. We had
obtained permission to spend it together, but since we
were so far apart, it was difficult to arrange. We were
still in the line, therefore, at Christmas.

The Austrians usually respected religious festivals.
On important ones they did not fire from their
trenches or permit their artillery to do so. But this
time our listening posts had managed to intercept an
enemy message referring to the fact that a mine was to
be exploded at midnight on Christmas Day. We believed that this mine had been dug in the rock below

196

our line, at the extreme left of the sector. Our instruments had registered the sound of drills since the end of October, and the higher command had been anxious about it ever since. If our positions were to be blown up at that point, the Austrians, taking advantage of the surprise, might well succeed not only in breaking the line there, and with it our communications, but in occupying the high point dominating the valley, between the two divisions. The right flank of our brigade would, as a result, be left completely in the air.

My battalion was more familiar with these positions than the others were, and the regimental commander ordered two of our companies, the 9th under Avellini, and my own, the 10th, to hold that part of the line on Christmas night. The regiment was being relieved on that very evening, and our two companies were left to carry on at this particularly dangerous point, where new troops might easily have found themselves at a loss.

After dusk the regiment went down into rest billets at Campomulo. The 9th company was left occupying the sector believed to be mined, while my company was ordered to be in reserve, quite close up, ready to counter-attack immediately after the explosion of the mine. Only we officers knew what was likely to happen. Our men merely grumbled at being the only ones to remain in the line, while the rest of the regiment was celebrating Christmas in billets. A more

generous ration than usual of chocolate and brandy
had aroused a certain amount of suspicion, but this
was dissipated by the thought that it was due merely
to the undertaking of additional duty.

Before taking up his position in the area where the
mine was believed to be, Avellini handed me a sealed
packet of letters. The appearance of the packet, and
the perfume it gave off, left little doubt in my mind
from whom they had come. I did not know anything
definite, but I was aware that Avellini was in love
with a girl. These were evidently the letters she had
written to him. With a smile which was meant to
excuse this happy secret, he said:

"It isn't anything very important, not a service matter. But if, tonight, I get buried by the mine, I should
like you to send off this packet to the person whose
address you will find in the first sealed envelope."

I hardly liked to ask him any questions. I did not
want to appear indiscreet, but, above all, I feared a
definite answer that might destroy the secret hope
that I had held on to amid so many anxieties and
doubts. Could the girl whose letters were entrusted
to me be the very one of whom I myself had been
thinking for so long? We had got to know her at the
same time, Avellini and I, in September, at Marostica,
near Bassano, a little town to which we had been sent
on service while the regiment was in rest billets at
Gallio. We had been presented to her by a brother

officer who was a relation of hers, and she had made a very deep impression on me. I hoped I had aroused a similar interest in her; I was almost sure I had. But Avellini had been able to see her again, and without me; and because my thoughts turned so often to the house where she lived, the doubt that she might prefer Avellini had constantly oppressed me. I had often intended to speak to him about it, but had never dared. That evening, when Avellini had handed me over the packet and was on the point of returning to the front line, I could resist no longer.

"Is she fair-haired?" I asked him.

He nodded.

"Is she beautiful?"

He replied happily, half-closing his eyes:

"Very beautiful."

I did not dare to question him further. But, I thought, why must it be she, of all people? Surely it might be someone else? Of course it might.

Avellini had good reason to believe he was in danger and to think that night might be his last. But apparently it had not occurred to him that I, too, would be running serious risks. In war it always seems to the man who is nearest the enemy that those behind him are in safety. At the moment I had not thought of it either, but as soon as I was alone, it struck me that the packet of letters was not much safer in my hands than in his. After the explosion of the mine, I should have to counter-attack, and no one could tell what might not happen then. I decided to put the packet in really safe custody.

Behind me, about a hundred yards away, where the valley opened out, there was a line of two redoubts, and an emplacement occupied by a mountain battery. I was on good terms with the commander, an artillery captain, whom I had known ever since he had come up to the front, and I had been in continual touch with him recently, discussing the plans for the construction of this small fort. On this very night I should have to keep in close contact with him, because if the mine were to explode, the fire of his guns would have to be co-ordinated with my company's counter-attack. Night had only just fallen. The mine was not due to be exploded until well after dark; not, in fact, until midnight, according to the intercepted signal.

I therefore went to see the captain of artillery, and found him in his small mess-room, which had been constructed behind the emplacement. Commanding officers of a battery in position, in the mountains, enjoy the same comforts as the commander of an infantry regiment in the line. The wooden walls were varnished and embellished with war pictures. The captain of artillery was seated at the table, which had not yet been cleared away, but his officers had finished their dinner and had gone back to their posts. He had a telephone and a couple of bottles at his elbow, one containing brandy and the other Benedictine, and he was sitting alone, smoking and drinking.

"They must be Mohammedans from Bosnia," he said, as soon as he saw me. "Imagine firing a mine on Christmas night! That's a nice kind of Christmas greeting. But I've got my guns so trained that, if they are Mohammedans, they'll join the Prophet this very night."

"I hope," I said, "that you won't take us for Bosnians and fire on us from the rear. Don't forget that as soon as the mine goes up, we shall begin our counterattack and shall be occupying the position on which you have trained your guns."

"Whom do you take us for? We shouldn't do a thing like that—we're not siege artillery. I've arranged for plenty of Very lights and rockets, and I shall be able to see everything from the observation post."

The conversation then turned on mountain artillery as compared with field artillery and medium and heavy guns, which were particularly inclined to miss their target and to fire on their own men. The artillery captain ordered coffee to be made. It was a specialty of his battery, the specialty consisting of three small glasses of the best brandy which were drunk in the following way: the first before the coffee, the second in the coffee, and the third after the coffee. From my earlier visits to him, he knew that I did not touch alcohol and he joked on the abstinence of one who must evidently be a victim of arteriosclerosis.

I showed him the sealed packet.

"If anything happens to me tonight, will you be so good as to give this packet to Avellini, who is the lieutenant in command of the 9th company? If he's no more fortunate than I am, you'll find, in this sealed envelope, the address of the person to whom the packet is to be sent."

The artillery captain had already drunk the first instalment of his special coffee.

"Love-letters?" he inquired.

I did not reply directly and he began to laugh loudly.

"What's there to laugh at?" I asked.

"You're right. There's nothing to laugh at. Matter for tears, more probably." But he went on laughing all the same.

"Do you believe in women?" he asked me at last.

"Why? Don't you?"

"I? Oh!"

He took up the brandy bottle, drank another glass, and then said:

"That's what I believe in."

"But that needn't prevent your believing, if the occasion should arise, in women too."

"I'm thirty-five," he said, "and I've been married for six years. I'm more experienced than you are."

"In such things experience doesn't count for much."

"Experience helps one to value life for what it is

and not for what one would like it to be. In comparison with me, you're only a boy. When a woman is a thousand miles away, the only possible thing to do is to forget her. Why have illusions? There's nothing else to be done. And this is the only way to forget."

We proceeded to drink our coffee.

"Because, if you don't forget, there's nothing else to do but to put a bullet through your head."

The artillery captain spoke most cheerfully. The brandy had certainly animated him, but he was also intoxicated by his own words. He spoke rapidly, as if he had been waiting a long time to find an opportunity for exchanging confidences. Taking a photograph out of his pocket-book he said to me:

"Look. She's beautiful. As beautiful as a woman can be. Yet she's not worth a bottle of brandy."

I took the photograph, but I did not have time to look at it, for he snatched it from me and, jumping up, threw it into the lighted stove.

I was embarrassed and did not know what to say, but he soon calmed down again and took my packet.

"You needn't worry," he said. "You can count on me." Then he changed the subject and began to talk to me of service matters, drinking as he did so.

We got up to go out. I was already at the door when he took me by the arm.

"You don't think I'm jealous?" he said.

"I never dreamed of it," I replied.

Together we visited the forward positions. The

gunners were at their pieces, with their officers. Everything was in order. I went back to my company. The men were in the dugouts, drinking and smoking; I sat down with them and waited for midnight.

At a quarter to twelve I formed the men into parties, so that they would be ready to leave the dugouts and to get into the communication trenches. As midnight drew nearer, the men began to realize that some unusual event was about to happen, and they looked at one another questioningly. I told them that a surprise attack was feared, and that we had to be ready to launch a counter-attack. But the nearer the dreaded moment approached, the more my thoughts seemed to stray from my company, from the mine, and from all the battle-front. "It must be she," I said to myself. "It can't be anyone else." And each time that the doubt returned, I found many pretexts for reassuring myself. "It can't be she; it's not possible." In my mind's eye I saw her again as I had caught sight of her for the first time, when I was going up to the front door of her home, which faced the street. She was at a window, and I saw her, with her fair curls falling over her forehead, yet not concealing her smiling eyes.

When I looked at my watch, midnight had passed. The mine had not exploded. I sent a runner to Avellini for news. He replied that he had seen nothing unusual, and that in the enemy trenches the routine appeared to be as usual.

We waited for dawn, our anxiety somewhat allayed. Had the interception posts made some mistake? Or had the Austrians played us a trick?

Next morning the two companies were relieved, and we rejoined the regiment at Campomulo. I had retrieved the packet of letters and given it back to Avellini.

The same evening the colonel invited us to dinner and told us we could go on leave on the following day. While we were having coffee he said:

"Tell me, honestly, have you ever experienced tenser moments in the whole course of the war than those last few minutes before midnight?"

Avellini hastened to reply.

"I was ready, of course; but my thoughts were elsewhere." And he looked at me, smiling, as if I alone could understand.

Chapter 23

AVELLINI AND I LEFT ON LEAVE AT THE SAME TIME. We went part of the way together because his family was in Piedmont and mine in Sardinia. My brother had, at the last moment, been prevented from coming, by service duties of some kind, and had had to put off his leave, so that I arrived home alone.

I found my father much aged. I had always thought of him as a vigorous man, but I realized at once that he was no longer his old self. He was depressed and did not hide his state of mind. We two were his only sons; both of us were in the infantry, and he had no illusions about our chances. He did not think that we could come home safe and sound from the war. He had neglected his own affairs, and I found the big old country house, once so full of life, almost deserted.

My mother seemed more courageous. I had often written to her, mailing my letters in places behind the lines, to make her think that I was in safety; but wounded men belonging to my regiment had talked of operations in which we had all taken part and had thus to a large extent destroyed the results of my little subterfuges. Nevertheless she seemed full of confidence and it was she who cheered even my father up.

I talked about the war with circumspection. But I succeeded at once in giving an idea of life in the front line as quite tolerable. My parents had imagined that we were perpetually engaged in terrific attacks. They had never for a moment supposed that we might live for months on end without fighting at all and without even seeing the enemy. They had no geographical idea of the front and, although the map showed that it was hundreds of miles long, they imagined that fighting in one sector must necessarily involve all the others. The war, as I described it to them, did not seem unendurable. Moreover, I could always make use of the argument that officers did not run the same risks as the men and that my brother was in a quiet part of the front. But whenever my father and I were alone, he told me his views quite frankly.

"I shall never see the end of this war. And I fear that you never will either."

One evening a relation of ours was dining with us, an infantryman who was convalescing from a wound. We had finished dinner and were having coffee. I had carefully avoided speaking of the war, but my father, more by way of making conversation than anything else, suddenly said to him: "What's your view, Antonio? When will the war come to an end?"

Antonio answered without hesitation:

"It won't come to an end. It's just butchery, and it'll never stop."

My mother did not understand, and said to him:

"What did you say it was?"

"Butchery," he repeated.

"For the officers too?" she asked.

"Yes. For the officers too."

When he had gone, I did all I could to prove that this was simply cowardice on Antonio's part.

My mother was always with me and I rarely went outside the house, because she was so anxious to have me near her. She treated me as if I were a child, to such an extent that at night, when I went to bed, she even wanted to help me take off my things and would often come back to kiss me more than once before going to her own room. In the morning it was always she who brought me my coffee while I was in bed. She insisted on my having it there, because that gave her a chance of being with me and of talking to me at length about all kinds of things.

This time my parents were not lucky over my leave. I had hardly been at home for four days when a telegram arrived from my commanding officer calling me back to the line for urgent and unforeseen service reasons. I said to myself that at last the time had come for our attack with the ladders and bridges; but to my parents I said I thought that I was wanted for the purchase of pack harness, for which, in the regiment,

I had the reputation of having greater skill than I really possessed. My father said nothing, and did not speak until it was time for me to go. To my great relief my mother remained calm and courageous as ever.

My father wanted to see me off and I therefore said good-bye to my mother, who stayed at home. Our parting was easy. She petted me and kissed me again and again without shedding a tear; even, at times, smiling. She showed so much confidence that I was astonished. I had never realized that she had such strength of spirit. My father, without saying a word or looking at us, continued to pace up and down, waiting for me.

We had left the house and gone about fifty paces, my father's arm in mine. I was laughing at his scanty knowledge of military regulations, telling him that he was making me behave in a most undisciplined fashion, because soldiers are not allowed to go arm-in-arm with anyone in public, not even with their fathers. Suddenly I remembered that I had left my cane behind. Leaving my father where he was, I hurriedly retraced my steps.

The front door was still open. I went in and called out: "Mother, I've forgotten my cane."

In the middle of the room, by an overturned chair, I found my mother lying limply on the stone floor sobbing. I lifted her up, but she had so completely given way to her grief that she was unable even to stand. When I tried to comfort her, she only wept the more. I must have remained some time with her, for suddenly I heard my father calling out impatiently:

"Have you got your cane? Hurry up or you'll miss your train."

I broke away from my mother, and ran back once more.

After travelling for three days without a stop, I reached the plateau. Avellini, too, had been recalled and had got back before I had.

It was indeed the attack with the bridges and ladders that was being got ready. The regiment was once more in the line. In order that I should lose no time, the transport officer gave me a mule, and in a few hours I was back in the trenches. Artillery was active in the whole sector.

It was about two or three o'clock in the afternoon when I got up to the front. My battalion was holding the same positions as during the previous spell of duty. A few sentries were on guard at the loopholes, perched up on wooden platforms. During the last few days more snow had fallen and the floor of the trenches had had to be raised to a new level. The sentries walked up and down on their platforms, like bricklayers on the scaffolding of a house in process of being built. The trunks of timber that supported the wooden superstructure made the trenches look like a slipway. The men themselves were arranged in echelon along the front line and communication trenches, waiting. Owing to the continual movement, the snow had melted at the bottom of the trenches and had formed a layer of slush, in which the men plunged about up to the knees. They seemed resigned and were all continually drinking from their brandy flasks. The moment I arrived, I smelt a fetid odour of mud and brandy, and I was reminded of Baudelaire's *"labyrintes fangeux"* in *"Le Vin des chiffoniers."*

The sky was overcast, and it looked as though more snow was coming.

The senior lieutenant, who had been commanding the company in my absence, came to meet me and tell me what news there was. Every man was present in the trenches, even those who had fever.

"You might just as well have stayed at home," he said, "and finished your leave in peace. We shan't be able to advance a single pace here today. The snow's up to my neck. To reach the enemy trenches I shall need an elevator."

He was a small man. But although I was considerably taller than he, I should not have been much better off. It seemed fantastic to propose an attack over ground like that.

I went to look for the battalion commander and found him in the mud, like everyone else. He was drinking too. It was the first time we had met, for he had just taken over, during the time in which I had been away on leave. He was a major, about fifty years of age, and had come to us straight from Libya. I was one of the few "veterans" in the regiment and he greeted me warmly, as if I were of equal rank. Having been suddenly transferred to the plateau from Africa, he confessed to me that he had not the remotest idea what trench warfare on our front was like.

"You needn't worry," I replied; "we know no more about it than you do."

"What's your opinion," he asked, "have we any chance of taking the enemy positions?"

"If the Austrians retire," I said, "it's possible that in a couple of hours, after we've dug paths through the snow, we might be able to reach the enemy trenches, even if we're frozen stiff in doing so. But if they don't retire, it looks to me extremely doubtful."

"Do you think they'll retire?"

"Why should they?"

"Then what about the ladders and bridges?"

"In weather like this they'll come in very useful. We'll burn them tonight to keep ourselves warm; otherwise we'll all die of cold."

The major was not in the mood for pleasantries. He realized only too well the difficulties the battalion would have to face in an attack, and was nervous and worried. In addition he found our brandy horrible.

The order to attack had still not come. Contrary to custom, the time had not been fixed ahead, for the divisional commander had decided to inform us of it at the last moment. This was "co-ordination of intellects," no doubt.

A runner arrived from regimental headquarters with a request that the major should go at once to the colonel. He turned pale.

"Now we're in for it," he said.

And he went, supporting himself with an alpenstock, his feet deep in the mud.

He was away for half an hour. When he returned, his face was wreathed in smiles. I saw him a little way off and I could not think what had caused this surprising change in him. Making his way through the men, who were standing back to allow him to pass, he called out to me:

"Nothing's going to happen after all!" And when he came up to me he said: "The attack's been put off."

"Put off?"

"Yes, put off. The general in command of the division has sent an order stopping it. It seems that it was to have been a demonstration. The general congratulates the officers and men on their good conduct during the day."

The artillery were still firing. Apparently the general had forgotten to let them know that the attack had been postponed. The men were ordered back into the dugouts, where they went on drinking as they had drunk before. Happiness and sorrow are very similar emotions.

That evening the major asked me to dine with him at battalion headquarters, and over coffee he grew confidential.

"I went through the whole of the Libyan war and I've taken part in many operations. I've been decorated for bravery, as you see, and I don't think I'm easily scared. Anyhow, not more easily than anyone else. I'm a soldier by profession, and it's probable that I shall reach a higher rank. But I can assure you that the things that have given me most satisfaction in my career are of the sort that happened today. We are professionals at warfare, and we can't grumble if we've got to fight. But when one is ready for an attack and at the last moment an order comes to call it off, I can tell you this: however courageous you may be, you'll thank your stars. Such moments, you can take my word for it, are the best you can experience in war."

As night fell, it became bitterly cold. The men were half-frozen and had no wood for their stoves. After a rapid consultation between the officers, we decided to use most of the planks and ladders for firewood.

Chapter 24

THE REGIMENT WAS SPENDING A FEW DAYS BEHIND THE lines near the village of Ronchi, with its headquarters higher up, at Campanella, about half a mile away. The three battalions were encamped in the few houses which were still intact and in groups of barracks. The men were tired and in low spirits. These brief spells of rest in places where they were still under enemy artillery fire, after turns of a month in the trenches, had a depressing effect on them. But there was hope of better things, for we had been told that we were at last to be sent down into the Venetian plain until the end of the winter. The issue of new equipment seemed to confirm the rumour, and even the most discontented began to cheer up.

I had just been promoted captain. Besides our battalion commander, Major Frangipane, another major, Melchiorri by name, had arrived from Africa and had taken over command of the 2nd battalion. The officers of my battalion invited him to dinner at our mess. It was a custom in the regiment to invite newly arrived officers to dinner, in order to get to know them. The major was pleased at the invitation and accepted it.

But when the day came, it did not seem a very appropriate one for conviviality. The regiment had just been ordered to hold itself in readiness to go back to the lines, after only three days' rest. We were all disgruntled. Our dreams of a long spell down in the plain had vanished, like so many before them. However, Major Melchiorri wanted to dine with us all the same. The men had finished eating their rations some time before and were in their barracks when we sat down at table. During dinner the conversation turned mainly on the subject of colonial warfare as compared with the Great War. Towards the end, only the two majors were talking, while the rest of us listened. Major Frangipane had been three years in Libya, and Major Melchiorri four or five in Eritrea. None of the rest of us had ever been in the colonies. Besides, with the exception of Avellini, we were all officers of the reserve. I was sitting by Major Melchiorri.

"The war in Europe," he said, "will be won only when our troops have been organized with the same disciplinary measures which we have used in the colonies with the Ascari. Obedience must be blind, as used to be rightly laid down in the army regulations of the glorious Piedmontese army. The mass must obey with their eyes shut, holding that it is an honour to serve their country on the battlefield."

"But our men," pointed out Major Frangipane, "are all Italian citizens like you and me; the Ascari are foreign mercenaries. The difference is a fundamental one."

"It is not so great as you imagine, and it is one that exists only in civil life. Once a citizen has put on a uniform he ceases to be a citizen and loses his political rights. He is nothing but a soldier and has no duties except military ones. The superiority of the German army is due to the fact that with them the soldier approaches more nearly to the ideal type represented by the Ascari. German officers really command their men."

"What do you mean by command? I've had a good deal of experience and I know well enough what it means to me. When in war-time I receive an order, I'm plagued by doubts as to whether there's not been some mistake. I've seen so many mistakes! And I've heard of plenty since I've been up here! When I myself give an order, I think it over well, in the fear of making a mistake myself. To command means to know how to command. That is to say, to avoid a number of errors that would lead to useless sacrifice and to demoralization of the men."

"But those in command do not make mistakes. To command means the right possessed by those of higher military rank to give an order. There are no such things as good orders and bad orders, or just and unjust orders. The order is always the same; and it presupposes an absolute right to call on the obedience of others."

"You might command a broomstick like that, my dear fellow, always supposing that you could lay your hands on it. But you'd never be able to command Italian, French, Belgian, or English troops in that way."

"It's because you've introduced philosophy into the army. That's the reason for our decline."

While the conversation went on, sustained by numerous bottles of wine, a noise began outside which sounded at first like the wind howling round the wooden barracks. Both majors stopped talking and listened. Major Frangipane got up and we all followed his example. The door opened and the officer on duty came in, looking extremely agitated.

"The regiment has mutinied! It started in the 2nd battalion and it's spread to the others. The men have left their billets and are demonstrating. One or two officers have been mishandled."

Without waiting for any orders from the major, we hurried out to get back to our men. The quarters belonging to my company, which happened to be nearest, could be reached in a few moments by going through the kitchen attached to the mess. Followed by the officers of my company, I ran through this way and found myself at once among the men.

The 10th company were quartered in a single

wooden barracks, which accommodated all four platoons. A wide corridor where the men could fall in
ran down the middle, and on either side were two
lines of berths, one above the other. The men were
standing about the corridor in groups, discussing matters with animation. The officers of the company
were behind me when I came in, and it was one of
the men who, being the first to catch sight of me,
loudly called the others to attention. Everyone stood
at attention at once. There was not a sound to be
heard in the whole place. I gave the order:

"Company, fall in, with rifles."

The men dispersed, hurrying off to obey the order.
I reckoned as follows: if the men were in a mood to
assault their officers and I ordered them to fall in with
their arms, I should no longer run the risk of a beating. If they had their rifles, they were likely to reflect
more before they acted, and, at the most, I should run
the risk of getting shot. I must confess that I would
rather have been shot by them than beaten.

In a moment the platoons had fallen in, with rifles,
in their correct positions. The senior platoon commander called them to attention and handed the company over to me. I gave the order to fix bayonets and
load. The order was promptly executed. I had the
roll called: no one was absent. If every man was present, it was clear my company had not mutinied. All
satisfaction must of necessity be personal and every-

one is entitled to feel it in his own way. The pleasure I felt at that moment I remember as one of the keenest in my life. Soldiers do not mutiny against their regimental, brigade, divisional, or Army Corps commanders. Their mutinous acts are directed, before all else, against the officers of their own units.

Outside, in the dark, the noise was increasing.

"We want to get out of the lines."

"Down with the war!"

"No more trenches!"

The 1st and 2nd battalions were encamped lower down, a few hundred yards away. From that direction a sound could be heard like that of a multitude on the march. It seemed probable that the two battalions had joined forces and were demonstrating together. I sent an officer to find out what he could, and he returned almost at once, saying that the men had come without their arms, but were destroying everything in their way.

Thousands of voices were shouting in unison: "Down with the war!"

I spoke a few words to the company, more to break the silence, which seemed to weigh us down, than because there was anything I wanted to say. I had little to talk about at the moment, and I knew very well that everyone's attention was riveted on the men who were demonstrating outside. The major came in, followed by the adjutant and the battalion orderlies. I called out: "Present arms" and told him that every man was present. The major was deeply distressed at what was happening.

"Men!" he exclaimed. "Men! What a day!"

He could say nothing else. When he went out I accompanied him, and he told me that two platoons of the 9th under Avellini had not mutinied, but that so far there was no information concerning the other two platoons which were quartered in another barracks. The 11th company had got out of hand, and the 12th were falling in again now that their commanding officer had put in an appearance. The machine-gun section was in line, with both their machine-guns. He was going to speak to the disbanded men and try to collect the whole battalion as soon as possible, in order to keep it apart from the rest of the mutineers.

The major disappeared in the direction of the 11th company and I followed him for a few yards until I came to the road. The night was dark, but enough light was coming from some windows to make it possible to see the road. Not far away a compact mass of men were advancing along it, shouting and throwing stones. Men from every unit were mixed together, but not one of them was armed. Two carts belonging to the battalion, which were standing by the roadside, were overturned and broken up like matchwood.

"We've had enough of the front line!"

"Down with the war!"

"No more lies!"

The mob was coming in our direction. I went back into the barracks, wondering what was going to happen.

The disorder grew worse. The head of the column had stopped in the street outside our barracks.

"Where's the 10th?"

"Come on out, comrades!"

"Come out and join us!"

There was no reply from the company. Then a single voice shouted from the mob:

"Leave them alone."

The shouting continued for some minutes and the column seemed to be hesitating. Then it went on, wheeled round, and disappeared along a road which led towards Campanella, in the direction of regimental headquarters. I went over to the other side of the barracks and opened a window. An icy wind was blowing down from the Campomulo valley. I leaned out.

A line of lights, in single file, was descending a footpath, which was used as a short cut from regimental headquarters to where the three battalions were encamped. It was evidently the regimental staff who were coming over to us and lighting their way with lanterns. Had they hurried, they would have come up against the mass who were demonstrating on the main road. But the lights stopped, and from where they stood a bugle call rang out above the whistling of the wind and the cries of the mutineers. The call was

"Officers, report." It was repeated, high-pitched and long drawn out. As the notes died away, the shouting of the men ceased also. For a moment there was only darkness and silence in the valley, and then an echo, far away towards Foza, Stoccaredo, and Col Rosso, took up the notes and repeated them, sadly and lingeringly, in the whole Asiago ampitheatre.

Why was the colonel ordering the officers to report? Why make them leave their men? Was it simply to give some sign of life, a reminder of the existence of headquarters? I did not think it wise to allow the officers to leave my company, so I sent only one of them to report.

The column of demonstrators had halted. I could see them, a large dark mass, standing motionless in the road. The colonel waited a few moments and then, giving up all idea of assemblying the officers, went towards the men, lantern in hand. When he reached them, the ranks opened and he passed into their midst. Raising the lantern so that all could see his face, he spoke to them in a clear voice:

"In your own interest, your colonel orders you back to your quarters."

A voice replied from one of the rear ranks:

"We've the right to a rest!"

"We all have that right," the colonel replied. "I, too, who am old, have a right to some rest. But now go back to your quarters. It is your own colonel who orders you to do so, and in your own interest."

The mass wavered. The front ranks retreated. The officer commanding the 6th company called out:

"6th company, fall in in your quarters."

Other officers did the same and tried to get their men together. The men in the front ranks began to scatter. But the men in the rear remained motionless, and isolated protests continued.

The colonel crossed the road. Having been informed that the 10th company had fallen in with their arms, he came towards my barracks. As he entered it, the cries outside began again:

"We want to go to a rest camp!"

"Down with the war!"

The colonel did not reply to the salute when the company presented arms, and said to me:

"Can I count on your company?"

"Yes, sir. Everything's in order."

"Can I count on them if I give them orders to go up to the lines at once?"

"Yes, sir."

"Can I count on them if I give them orders to act against the mutineers?"

This conversation between the colonel and me took place in front of everyone. We were almost in the middle of the company, which was drawn up in two ranks, in such a way that I could see half the men from in front. These men were fixedly watching my face, and my face only.

"I don't think so, sir."

"Answer yes or no."

"No, sir."

The colonel went out. In the street the noise continued.

Chapter 25

BEFORE TEN O'CLOCK ALL DETACHMENTS OF THE THREE
battalions had gone back to barracks. Order had been
re-established. At midnight we officers of the 3rd battalion were still sitting talking in the mess. The major and the adjutant were at regimental headquarters,
and the officers on duty for that night were also absent,
one from each company. We were discussing, among
ourselves, the events of the evening. Avellini was on
such a friendly footing with us that the fact that he
was a regular officer and that we were of the reserve
made no difference to us. I can still remember the
conversation, and I can summarize it in this way:

OTTOLENGHI: My company were all right, or nearly so.
Only one idiot wanted to go out with a machine-gun
and fire it into the blue. I told him that if he moved,
I'd shoot him. One machine-gun indeed! If my machine-guns are taken out, they all have to go together.
If one's to fire, they all must. And if my machine-gun
section is to take part in a demonstration, it must do
it *en bloc,* with officers, non-commissioned officers,

and men. In that case I shall be in the mutiny myself. And some fine day I dare say it'll happen. Because I agree entirely with the unit who did protest. They were perfectly right, but they chose a bad moment. To mutiny at night, and without arms! What a blunder!

AVELLINI: You're mad.

THE COMMANDER OF THE 12TH COMPANY: You talk like a lunatic!

OTTOLENGHI: If you want to mutiny, you ought to do it by day, and with arms, choosing a moment when everyone's with you. All officers of lower rank!

THE COMMANDER OF THE 12TH COMPANY: A grand program! But what about the others?

OTTOLENGHI: What others? Surely you don't want to mutiny side by side with the generals?

THE COMMANDER OF THE 12TH COMPANY: If that's what you think, you ought to resign your commission.

OTTOLENGHI: But whether I'm an officer or in the ranks, I should have to fight just the same. I can't get out of it, so I prefer to serve as an officer.

AVELLINI: You've taken an oath as an officer. So either you're not speaking seriously, or you don't take the oath seriously.

OTTOLENGHI: Of course I don't. Whether you're an officer or a soldier, you're forced to swear in, individually or collectively. If I hadn't taken the oath as an officer, I should have to take it as a private. It comes to the same thing. The laws of our country excuse no one but cardinals and bishops from military service. The oath is therefore nothing but a formality which we are obliged to take in the course of our compulsory military service.

AVELLINI: A man of honour will not give his oath if he doesn't mean to keep it.

THE COMMANDER OF THE 12TH COMPANY: You're not only mad, you're disloyal.

OTTOLENGHI: Can you maintain that if I'm taken against my will, by main force, and compelled to swear, it's dishonourable to make a mental reservation not to keep my oath?

AVELLINI: Who's going to take you by main force? No one can compel your conscience.

THE COMMANDER OF THE 12TH COMPANY: If you've got one.

OTTOLENGHI: No one, you say? In war-time, if I were called to the colours and refused to take the oath, I'd be handed over to a military tribunal who'd shoot me at the first opportunity. Taking the oath is a necessary lie, a legitimate act of self-defence. That being so, and since there's no escape from it, I prefer to serve as an officer rather than in the ranks.

AVELLINI: Why?

OTTOLENGHI: If a favourable occasion were to arise, I want to have a better chance to be able to profit by it.

A SECOND LIEUTENANT: Have a drink and turn in.

OTTOLENGHI: I shan't simply have a rifle and a bayonet, but a hundred rifles and a hundred bayonets and also—here's to you—a couple of machine-guns.

THE COMMANDER OF THE 11TH COMPANY: And against whom do you propose to use them?

OTTOLENGHI: Against our commanders.

THE COMMANDER OF THE 11TH COMPANY: And then? Do you aspire to become the commander-in-chief?

OTTOLENGHI: I aspire merely to direct the fire of my weapons. On that day, whenever it comes, sights down, independent fire! And I'll start with our divisional commander, whoever he may be, because each one of them is always worse than the last.

THE COMMANDER OF THE 11TH COMPANY: And then?

OTTOLENGHI: Then forward! Up the scale! Forward in good order and with discipline. Forward, but only in a manner of speaking, because our true enemies are not in front of us. We must about turn, therefore, first of all, and then we can go ahead.

A SECOND LIEUTENANT: That is to the rear?

OTTOLENGHI: Of course. We must go on, on until we get to Rome. That's where enemy General Headquarters are.

THE COMMANDER OF THE 11TH COMPANY: And then?

OTTOLENGHI: Isn't that enough?

A SECOND LIEUTENANT: It'll be a grand outing.

OTTOLENGHI: The people will seize power.

THE COMMANDER OF THE 10TH COMPANY: But if you march our army on Rome, do you think the German and Austrian armies will stay where they are? Or do you imagine that, to please our popular government, the Germans will go back to Berlin, and the Austrians and Hungarians to Vienna and Budapest?

OTTOLENGHI: I don't care what the others'll do. It's enough for me to know what I intend.

THE COMMANDER OF THE 10TH COMPANY: That's all very fine, but it doesn't throw much light on the problem. What would your march to the rear really mean? An enemy victory, obviously. Can you believe that a military victory over us wouldn't become a political victory too? In our wars of independence, whenever the enemy was victorious, did they not carry, on their bayonets, the Bourbons to Naples and the Pope to Rome? When the Austrians beat us, at Milan, in Lombardy, and in the Veneto, did they ever allow a popular government to stay in power? If our enemies are victorious now, Italy will again find herself under reactionary foreign domination. Surely that's not what you want?"

OTTOLENGHI: I certainly don't. But all the same I'm against this war, which is nothing but a horrible massacre. Isn't civil war just the same?

THE COMMANDER OF THE 11TH COMPANY: To tell the truth, I don't want either.

THE COMMANDER OF THE 10TH COMPANY: Ottolenghi

doesn't agree with that. He hates the one, but exalts the other. But aren't they both the same?

OTTOLENGHI: No, they are not. Revolution means progress for the people and all the oppressed. War is nothing but useless slaughter.

THE COMMANDER OF THE 10TH COMPANY: Useless, you say? Some of us here were at universities. At mine we burned the speeches of William II, who invoked the war god at every opportunity and who seemed to want to feed his subjects on nothing but guns and bayonets. Useless slaughter indeed! If we hadn't resisted the Central Powers, today in Italy and Europe we'd all be doing the goose-step to the sound of a drum.

OTTOLENGHI: Each side is as bad as the other.

THE COMMANDER OF THE 12TH COMPANY: And democracy? And liberty? What would your country be without them?

OTTOLENGHI: A fine kind of democracy and liberty we've got!

THE COMMANDER OF THE 10TH COMPANY: Still, it's on their account that many of us have been in favour of intervention and have taken up arms and are sacrificing our lives.

OTTOLENGHI: The slaughter is not worth the sacrifice.

THE COMMANDER OF THE 12TH COMPANY: And what of Italy's interest?

OTTOLENGHI: What of us? Aren't we Italy?

THE COMMANDER OF THE 10TH COMPANY: Have the ideals that brought us into the war ceased to exist because war is a massacre? If we are convinced that we must fight, our sacrifices are worth while. I agree that we are all tired and the men have loudly proclaimed the fact today. That's only human nature. At a certain moment we grow discouraged and begin to think only of ourselves. The instinct for self-preservation becomes paramount, so that most of us would like to see the war ended, ended in any kind of way, because its end would ensure our physical safety. But is that sufficient justification? If it were, wouldn't a handful of brigands have the power to keep us continually in subjection, with complete impunity, simply because we were afraid of being killed? If injustice and violence were never to meet with resistance, it would be the end of our civilization.

OTTOLENGHI: I'm prepared to admit that, for the sake of argument.

THE COMMANDER OF THE 10TH COMPANY: Then you must admit that it's a duty to defend one's own ideals even at the risk of one's life. The argument that one is tired and has had enough of horrors is not sufficient to condemn war. The men mutinied this evening. Were they right or wrong? They may be either the one or the other; or perhaps both at once. The mass only sees an immediate advantage. But what would happen if their example was generally followed in the army?

OTTOLENGHI: Their conduct was justified, because the war wouldn't be the ghastly slaughter it is if it weren't for the utter incompetence of our leaders.

THE COMMANDER OF THE 11TH COMPANY: That is true.

THE COMMANDER OF THE 12TH COMPANY: Yes. Ottolenghi's right there.

A GROUP OF SECOND LIEUTENANTS: Quite right.

AVELLINI: I can't deny that, either.

OTTOLENGHI: You see! You are all forced to admit I've right on my side.

THE COMMANDER OF THE 10TH COMPANY: Our political and military leaders were not prepared when we came into the war. But that's no reason why we should lay down our arms.

OTTOLENGHI: Our generals might have been sent by our enemies to destroy us.

A GROUP OF SECOND LIEUTENANTS: True enough.

THE COMMANDER OF THE 11TH COMPANY: Unfortunately, it is.

OTTOLENGHI: And a band of speculators who are protected by Rome have grown up round them and are making money out of our lives. We had an example the other day when boots were issued to the battalion. Very fine boots they were, too. They had "Long live Italy" printed on the soles in the national colours. But after a day's wear in the mud, we found that these soles were of paper varnished to look like leather.

A GROUP OF SECOND LIEUTENANTS: That's true.

OTTOLENGHI: The boots don't matter. What is terrible is that they have varnished our very lives, stamped the name of our country on us and driven us like sheep to the slaughter.

The door was opened, and the conversation stopped. Major Frangipane came in, followed by Major Melchiorri and their two adjutants. We stood up.

"I am proposing," Major Melchiorri said, "to have ten soldiers in each company shot at once. The position's grave, and it's necessary to make an example."

"Capital punishment cannot be enforced in the case of men who have not had recourse to arms," our major pointed out.

"But the divisional commander agrees with me."

We listened to the two majors without saying a word.

Ottolenghi turned to us and said:

"I'm in favour of the execution of the divisional commander."

Major Frangipane was tired and depressed.

"We'd better turn in," he said. "One officer on duty with each company will be enough. By tomorrow we shall know what decision has been come to tonight by the general in command of the Army Corps."

Chapter 26

THE REGIMENT WAS ONCE MORE IN THE TRENCHES. THE general in command of the Army Corps had been of the same opinion as the brigade commander and had rejected the proposal to apply capital punishment to the mutineers. Only seven men out of all the privates and non-commissioned officers involved were handed over to a military tribunal and condemned to terms of imprisonment. They were later allowed to serve in other regiments that were in the line in order to earn remission of their sentences by good conduct.

As the spring sun grew slowly warmer in the mountains, the level of the snow began to fall. And as it fell, the parapets of our trenches had to be lowered too. The great bastions lost their towers, and the wooden staging was dismantled. Every week we cleared away a layer of sandbags filled with snow, and the line of loopholes once more descended, little by little, towards ground level.

With the return of good weather, plans of attack were considered again. Heavy batteries were springing up, all over the place, like mushrooms. The whole range of mountains behind us, encircling the Asiago plateau, contained an unending chain of masked batteries. The field and mountain batteries nearest to us were merely the advance guard of that tremendous array of guns. This time important forces were to be employed. Still more batteries continued to arrive by way of the roads from Congo and Foza, which had been constructed during the winter. Trench-mortar batteries were installed behind the front line. Long lines of trucks laden with munitions were arriving day and night from the Venetian plain. The engineers were working at two great land mines, one of which was to be exploded beneath Casara Zebio, and the other at point 1496, beneath Monte Interrotto. Active warfare was once more on the way. But in April the snow still lay deep round all our positions, although it had nearly disappeared on the plateau itself.

My battalion was resting down the line, according to the usual routine, at Ronchi. Major Frangipane, who had been wounded by a shell splinter, was in hospital and I was in command of the battalion.

One morning Lieutenant Ottolenghi came to me for permission to make an excursion with the skiing detachment belonging to the battalion. As he was still in command of the battalion machine-gun section, he really had nothing to do with the skiers, but during the winter we had both been keenly practicing skiing and had grown proficient at it. He had become a real devotee. The battalion detachment of skiers constituted a special section commanded by a sergeant. They had attended a course at Bardonecchia and were, according to general army instructions relating to warfare in the mountains, supposed to provide patrols for reconnaissance beyond our lines. But the distance between our trenches and those of the enemy was so small that it did not provide enough room for patrols to operate on skis, and the few experiments made discouraged their use even after dark. The terrain was, in addition, strewn with uprooted trees and strands of barbed wire and had become difficult going. During the day there was no single point at which our patrols could leave the line unobserved, though at night we could occasionally send men out on snow-shoes. In the morning, however, their tracks were always visible and the enemy was only put more on his guard. The skiing detachment was therefore of no use to us. The battalion commander sometimes sent it off on trips to Campomulo, Croce di Longaro, Monte Fior, and Foza, to keep them in training, but he had never made use of them beyond our lines.

Ottolenghi had occasionally taken part in these excursions, as I had. His request therefore accorded with our usual winter routine; but the necessities of the service forced me to tell him that he could take only half the detachment.

Ottolenghi demurred. "I can't do anything worth

while with only half," he said. "I want to undertake a real battle exercise with the skiers, which will include the throwing of bombs and hand-grenades. Without the whole detachment it's impossible to carry out a real patrol attack. We are on the eve of a big operation, and I'd like to train a good detachment of specialists, like our skiers."

As I was also much interested in training of this kind I finally gave way. Ottolenghi went off with the whole detachment of ten men, one corporal, and one sergeant. Their haversacks were loaded with bombs. Later on I received a report of their doings.

"The orders of the battalion commander," Ottolenghi had said to his men, "are that we shall carry out an operation of war, quickly and secretly. It will be a test of efficiency. In a short time now, large-scale operations will begin, and we must be prepared. This time it's be real warfare, and not an affair with ladders and bridges. But a warlike operation like the one we have orders to undertake today presupposes an enemy. Who is the enemy? That is the question. The Austrians? Evidently not. Our natural enemies are our own generals. If His Excellency General Cadorna were to be in the neighborhood, he'd be our chief enemy and it would only be a matter of getting on his tracks. Unfortunately, however, he's nowhere near. Nor is the general commanding the army on this front. Even the general commanding the Army Corps is a long way off, well dug in at the foot of the plateau. Generals of high rank hate snow. Who else is there, then? Only the small fry. The divisional commander, for instance—of small importance, but perfect of his kind. A man of rare intelligence. Very rare."

The skiers knew Ottolenghi well. His reputation had spread, in the course of time, to the entire battalion. They therefore listened to him with much enjoyment.

"All the same," said the sergeant, half in jest and half in earnest, "we aren't expected to carry out a bomb attack on the general, are we, sir?"

"Not directly. We won't attack the general personally, although that would certainly be a notable advance towards victory. The orders of the battalion commander are as follows: 'Do whatever you wish, but spare the general's life.' That being the case, we must obey. We will therefore make a daring lightning attack on the divisional food storehouse and carry off as much plunder as possible."

The excitement of the skiers was unbounded. Ottolenghi explained to them in detail the plan he had thought out; after which they all started off enthusiastically to put it into execution, Ottolenghi at their head.

The food store was contained in a large wooden hut, situated not far from the road leading from Camponella to Foza, in a small valley which protected it from enemy observation. Snow still lay deep all around it. Ottolenghi and the skiers knew the place well, as they had often passed it on previous excursions. The store contained a huge quantity of foodstuffs for the troops and for the officers' messes of all units included in the Division. It contained, in large quantities, bottles of wine and liqueurs, hams, sausages of various kinds, and cheeses.

The detachment made a wide detour in order to take the store by surprise from above and to make it impossible to trace where the ski tracks had come from. Towards sunset they arrived in a body at a spot about three quarters of a mile above the road. From there, keeping together, they descended in the direction of the store. When they were within a few hundred paces of it, the detachment divided. Ottolenghi, the sergeant, and six men formed one party, the "tactical," which was again divided into two groups; the remaining five men, with the corporal, formed a second party, the "logistical." It was Ottolenghi who thus designated the two parties. The first was intended to make a frontal attack on the store, and the second to take it from the rear.

The first party started down the hill, throwing their bombs and hand-grenades and shouting with all their might. The noise at once attracted the attention of the soldiers on duty at the store. They all rushed out into the open. The sight that met their eyes was certainly an extraordinary one. The skiers

were hurling their missiles and at the same time ma-
nœuvring with consummate skill. Shooting swiftly
about through clouds of smoke from the bombs, and
to the accompaniment of deafening explosions, they
succeeded in giving the impression of two patrols
furiously attacking each other. To the peaceful and
astonished soldiers of the lines of communication it
was not obvious that the bombs which burst on the
surface of the snow were merely smoke bombs and
therefore almost innocuous to those who threw them,
while the more dangerous ones were exploding much
farther away, and half-buried in deep snow. It was a
remarkable and realistic glimpse of warfare to the
men guarding the store, who had always been attached to the supply services in the rear and had never
witnessed any sort of engagement. This one was altogether terrifying. For a moment it looked to them
as if these desperate combatants would all heroically
blow one another to pieces before their eyes, and their
admiration gave place to horror.

While this engagement was taking place before the
petrified guardians of the magazine, the "logistical"
party was acting with no less daring on the flank. The
five men forming it took off their skis as they reached
the building, jumped through the windows, and in a
few minutes came out again, all heavily laden. Ottolenghi had equipped them with baskets and haversacks, which they had proceeded to cram with sau-

sages, hams, and bottles. Having put on their skis again, they rapidly disappeared up the valley opposite.

The operation had succeeded brilliantly, in every particular.

That night at mess Ottolenghi produced four bottles of liqueur in honour of his grandfather's birthday. Why his grandfather's? I asked myself in some surprise. But it was not till the following morning that my suspicions began to be aroused.

An order was circulated from divisional headquarters describing the incident and requesting all subordinate commanders to take immediate steps for the discovery of those responsible. The general demanded that "banditry" of the kind should be relentlessly punished. I had hardly finished reading the order when I found that, according to the daily report, Sergeant Melino, of the 10th company, had been wounded. He had been struck in the leg by a fragment of a grenade, and the regimental surgeon had seen him and excused him from duty for a week. Sergeant Melino happened to be the sergeant who was attached to the skiers. He had been in my company since the beginning of the war and I had promoted him lance-corporal, corporal, and sergeant. In fact I had chosen him myself to attend the course at Bardonecchia, and I had always had a very high opinion of him. I went at once to see him, and found him lying down, resting his bandaged leg.

"What about this wound of yours?" I asked. "Can you explain how you have been wounded by a hand-grenade while the battalion is in rest billets?"

There were some men near us, and the sergeant signed to me to send them away, which I did.

"Why all this mystery?" I demanded.

The sergeant told me everything. It appeared that the hams, the sausages, and a number of bottles of wine had been distributed in secret that same night in the battalion by the skiers belonging to the different companies. By now probably no trace of them remained.

Things looked like becoming complicated. I called the company surgeon and told him to hold up the official notification of the sergeant's wound for the time being. Then I went to put some questions to Ottolenghi.

"Since when," I inquired, "has the stealing of hams and sausages been a way of making revolutions?"

"In all revolutions," he countered, "there's a lot of stealing done."

"Of hams?"

"Yes, of hams, among other things."

"You've made the battalion carry out a fine sort of operation. Look at the order issued by the divisional commander; and the report on Sergeant Melino's wound! How's the battalion going to get out of this mess?"

"What are you going to do about it?" he asked.

"An operation of this kind can only increase the prestige of the battalion. You can't deny that it was splendidly carried out. If I'd had a platoon with me, I could have emptied the whole storehouse, sugar and coffee included. What would you say if we undertook a similar coup against the divisional commander in person? Would you like us to? You've only to say the word! I can assure you that no one will ever find anything out. We could take him prisoner and keep it a profound secret. The soldiers would be only too glad of a chance of amusing themselves. What do you say?"

I made the officers fall in. I read them the divisional order, and ordered immediate investigations. Some hours later I received a written report on the result. It was negative. All subordinate officers were convinced that it was impossible for their men to have taken any part whatever in the escapade. Ottolenghi's report was likewise negative.

Just before it was time for mess, I saw Avellini.

"Between ourselves, do you know anything about this business of the divisional storehouse?"

"I know that my men have been eating ham and sausages all night. Some have even got indigestion. They've been so devilish thirsty that I've had to give them some bottles of wine; it seems they didn't succeed in capturing many."

The report of the officer in command of the regiment was also negative.

Chapter 27

A BIG OPERATION WHICH WAS TO INVOLVE THE WHOLE army was now in active preparation. It was certain that our brigade would be allotted an important part in it. Officers were issued with maps of the area as far as Cima Dodici and Val Lagarina. Every now and then isolated shots from the guns showed that new batteries were finding their ranges. Heavy guns had also been brought up to their positions. The sector held by our regiment alone contained about twenty batteries, arranged in groups.

To rest the men after the rigours of the winter and to put them in good heart for what was to come, the brigade was sent down to a rest camp on the plain. Our battalion went into billets at Vallonara, at the foot of the plateau.

We were not there for long—only a week, in fact. But that week was an enchantment. For a whole year, ever since we had been at Aiello, our men had never been quartered among the civilian population. Weariness and discontent vanished in an instant and everyone, in dealing with civilians, assumed a self-confident and protective air. Were we not the saviours of the country? Had it not been for us, this whole population would have had to leave their homes and their fields and take refuge in the interior, to a wretched existence on what the State would allow them. No wonder the young women gave the soldiers such admiring glances!

For the men of the battalion those days were among the happiest of the whole war. Vallonara was a small village of only a few hundred inhabitants, but in the fertile countryside between Bassano and Marostica there were innumerable grassy meadows, where the peasants pastured their cows. When the men were at liberty, they would gather together in sections or in isolated groups about the fields, in festive mood. They and the villagers tried to outdo one another in liberality. Anything the men possessed they were ready to share. For the time being they were the lords of the plain. It is true that in every company there were some who never stirred out, who were gloomy and solitary, with no liking for such convivialities. They stayed where they were, lounging about the camp and avoiding their fellows. But the greater part, who were young, scoured the country like knights errant, in search of happiness. In the warm and glowing afternoons of that exceptional May, the whole countryside resounded with *stornelli* and popular songs, the carefree voices of the men blending with those of the women. How delightful life had become again! One day, as I was walking through a vineyard with my head in the air inspecting a telephone wire belonging to the battalion, I stumbled on a soldier of the 10th company who was with a young peasant girl. Stretched out on the grass, beneath a bower of vine leaves, they were confiding their secrets to each other. Had I seen them in time, I should have avoided them, but the encounter was as unexpected for me as it was for them. The man scrambled to his feet, came to attention, and saluted. He was red in the face and looked embarrassed. At his side, very slowly, and with quiet grace, the girl got up too. Fair-haired and slender, she seemed fairer than ever as she stood beside the dark-skinned Sardinian. She looked at me for a moment with a shy smile, then lowered her eyes and clung to the man as if seeking his protection. I took out my purse, gave him ten lire, and said:

"Your commanding officer is glad to see you in such good company!"

The man took the money, still embarrassed, and the girl smiled, swaying slightly as she stood, her large eyes wide open and full of gratitude. How happy they were! I, too, felt happy.

Happy and unhappy at the same time. I had my own emotional problems, and I did not know their solution.

At that time Avellini was in the seventh heaven. The people we knew in Marostica often invited us to tea; but I was still in command of the battalion, and my time was taken up, even in the afternoon, with many service duties, so that I could not often accompany him. He was freer and always went when invited.

A personal success added to his happiness. The brigade commander had deputed him to give a lecture to the officers of the brigade on company tactics in mountain warfare. He had got up his subject with enthusiasm, and I had helped him with it by putting my longer experience of warfare at his disposal. We both hated lectures even more than heavy guns but Avellini did extremely well. The general congratulated him and spoke of him at divisional headquarters as a regular officer with a future. Avellini could scarcely contain his joy. After the lecture he told me in confidence of his hopes for the future. He liked nothing better than his military career. He wanted to distinguish himself as a company commander, to enter the Staff College, get on the General staff, command a battery of artillery, then an infantry battalion, and go on studying, studying, always. To be able to serve his country in this way and to have a part in building up an army, a great army, in order to revive its military glories, was his ambition. He did not seem to ask anything else of life.

That afternoon, we both went to Marostica to tea, and it was he who carried off the honours.

Our period of rest passed like a dream.

Chapter 28

ON THE 8TH OF JUNE THE AUSTRIANS, WHO WERE anticipating an offensive on our part, fired the mine beneath Casara Zebio. It was this mine that had kept us in the line on Christmas Eve. When it exploded, it destroyed our trenches and buried the troops that were holding them, together with some officers of a regiment which happened to have stopped there during a reconnaissance. The incident was regarded by our men as a bad omen.

On the 10th our artillery opened fire at five a.m. The big operation, which was to extend along a front of over thirty miles, from Val d'Assa to Cima Caldiera, had begun. On the plateau there were, including heavy trench mortars, not less than a thousand pieces of artillery. A terrific din, with explosions which seemed to come from the very bowels of the earth, shook the whole front. The ground itself trembled beneath our feet. It was not the noise of artillery fire, but a veritable inferno that the guns had let loose.

We had always complained of the lack of artillery, but now we had plenty.

The troops had been withdrawn from the trenches, which were occupied only by some covering parties. The 1st and 2nd battalions of our regiment had been brought under cover in big dugouts that had been constructed during the winter. All four companies of the 3rd battalion were in the open, holding the line of the two redoubts in the rear. The small dugouts that had been constructed there were occupied by the gunners of the mountain artillery, whose battery was in the neighbourhood, and by our machine-gunners.

The enemy artillery replied to our batteries with their heavy guns, but they did not fire on our front line. Only our own artillery did that.

What happened has never been properly cleared up. A few batteries armed with naval ordnance of 149 and 152 mm. started to fire on us. The battalions in the dugouts did not suffer, but from the beginning mine sustained heavy losses. Major Frangipane, who had just returned from leave, was one of the first to be hit and I reassumed the command of the battalion. The line joining the two redoubts, which my battalion had been ordered to hold, was knocked to pieces. It had been constructed to resist attack from the front and not from the rear. The 9th and the 10th companies lost half their effectives. Lieutenant Ottolenghi brought his machine-gunners out of the dugout, shouting:

"We must attack the batteries that are firing on us and shoot the gunners down."

I saw him in time, went up to him, and forced him to go back to his post. Then I made the companies fall back a few hundred yards and informed the regimental commander. There were already many casualties in the battalion, and we had not enough stretchers to take the wounded back to the dressing-station.

While I was going from section to section, I passed an artillery colonel, followed by two lieutenants. Bareheaded, his revolver in his hand, he was shouting between the shell-bursts:

"You're killing us! You're killing us!"

I went to meet him and suggested to him that he should make use of my officers to transmit an order to the battery to alter the range. He did not even realize that I was an officer and, without answering me, continued to shout out unconnected phrases. The two lieutenants followed him without speaking, a lost look on their faces. I began to lose my self-control. Brigade headquarters had been temporarily moved up to the rear of my battalion within a short distance of where we were. I hurried off there as fast as I could and found the general in command of the brigade sitting in a small dugout, a telephone receiver in his hand. I rapidly told him what was happening. He listened calmly,—much too calmly. I spoke with agitation, but he remained indifferent. In my excitement, I exclaimed:

"We're making a pretty good hash of it today, sir!"
The general jumped to his feet. I thought he was going to throw me out; but he came towards me and embraced me with tears in his eyes.

"My dear fellow, it's our profession," he said.

I then learned that he had been sending runners and written orders for more than an hour, but in vain. I went back to my battalion in despair.

In the sector held by the 2nd battalion even worse things were happening. Major Melchiorri had installed himself in a small dugout alongside the large one in which the 5th company were taking cover. He had been much shaken by the firing of the artillery. In Africa he had never witnessed warfare on such a scale, and his nerves could not stand up to it. Having drunk one whole bottle of brandy, he had sent all round the battalion to try to unearth another. He was still waiting for the second bottle when he heard the noise of a disturbance in the dugout which housed the 5th company.

This dugout was the worst constructed of all those belonging to the regiment. It had been one of the first to be made, before the mining company had had sufficient experience of work of that kind. It was long horizontally, but not dug deep enough. It could contain an entire company, but it was almost on ground level; and though strong enough to stand a bombardment by light artillery, it was no good against heavy guns. At any rate, the men who were inside it were

under the impression that it was not. That morning
our own ordnance of 149 and 152 mm. had made a
special target of it. A few of their shells which had
exploded in the entrance had killed some men as well
as the captain in command of the company. Whole
batteries had continued to cover it with salvoes, until
the company, stunned by the continuous hammering
they had undergone, suffocated by the fumes from the
shell-bursts, and deprived of their commanding officer, were no longer able to stand the ordeal. The men
thought that the roof would fall at any moment and
bury them all. They wanted to get out into the open.
There were cries of "Out of here!"

Major Melchiorri heard the shouting and sent to
find out what was going on. When he realized that
the men wanted to leave the dugout, he was overcome
with anger. The orders stated that the troops were
not to leave the posts assigned to them until the time
fixed for the attack.

"We're in face of the enemy," the major shouted,
"and I order you to stay where you are. Anyone who
moves must take the consequences!"

The second bottle of brandy now arrived and the
major forgot the 5th company. The bombardment
went on. After a short time the company rushed out
of the dugout and collected in a lateral depression in
the ground that was not under artillery fire.

The major thought that he was confronted by mutiny. Indeed, he was convinced of it. A whole com-

pany, a short time before zero hour, close to the enemy, and with their weapons in their hands, had refused obedience. For him the matter was clear. The only thing to do therefore was to take immediate action of the most rigorous kind and to punish the mutineers. He left his dugout in a rage, made the company fall in, and ordered decimation.

The 5th company obeyed his orders without question. While the adjutant was numbering the men and falling out one in ten for immediate execution, news of the affair spread to the other companies of the battalion, and various officers came over. The major explained to them that he intended to avail himself of the instructions issued by the high command on the subject of capital punishment under exceptional circumstances. The officer commanding the 6th company was among those present. As Lieutenant Fiorelli, he had commanded the 6th during the operations in the previous August, and after having recovered from the wounds he had received on that occasion, and having been promoted captain, he had once more taken over command of the company. He pointed out that the crime of mutiny in face of the enemy had not been committed, and that even if it had, Major Melchiorri had no right to order the company to be decimated without the concurrence of the officer in command of the regiment.

The views expressed by Captain Fiorelli merely

angered the major. He picked up his revolver and covered him with it.

"Hold your tongue," he said, "or you'll become an accessory to the mutiny and subject to the same penalty. I am the responsible officer here. On the field of battle I alone have power of life and death over men under my command who break military discipline."

Captain Fiorelli remained unmoved. He quietly, and repeatedly, asked permission to speak, but the major would not allow it.

Every tenth man had now fallen out, and twenty soldiers were waiting, separated from the rest of the 5th company.

The major ordered the men called to attention, and stood at attention himself. The noise made by the artillery was deafening and he had to shout to make himself heard by everyone. He spoke with great gravity.

"In the name of His Majesty the King, supreme commander of the army, I, Major Ruggero Melchiorri, who rightfully hold the command of the 2nd battalion of the 399th infantry regiment, relying on the exceptional measures promulgated by His Excellency General Cadorna, Chief of the General Staff, order the execution of the men belonging to the 5th company who have been guilty of armed mutiny in face of the enemy."

The major was by this time in an exalted state and was only listening to himself. But this state of mind was not shared by the other officers present, nor by the 5th company, nor by the twenty men who had been condemned to death. In our brigade no execution had ever been carried out. This decimation was so precipitate and extraordinary an occurrence as to appear outright impossible. But it is not essential for everyone to believe in a play in order for it to go on. On this occasion it was Major Melchiorri who held the centre of the stage; and he was already almost carried away by his own performance.

He ordered Captain Fiorelli to take command of the firing squad, which was to be a platoon of his own company.

"I am a company commander," Captain Fiorelli objected, "so I cannot command a platoon."

"Then you refuse to carry out my orders?" the major asked.

"I do not refuse to carry out any order. I'm simply pointing out that I am a captain and not a lieutenant; the commander of a company, and not of a platoon."

"Will you or will you not obey the orders I have given you?" cried the major, again pointing his revolver at Captain Fiorelli's chest.

"No, sir," replied Fiorelli.

"You won't?"

"No, sir."

The major hesitated for a moment, but did not fire.

"Very well, then," he said curtly, "order a platoon of your company to fall in."

Fiorelli repeated the order to the second lieutenant in command of the 1st platoon of the 6th. A few moments later the platoon left the dugout and fell in. The second lieutenant then received the order to load from the major, and repeated it to his men; but their rifles were already loaded. In front of them, motionless and bewildered, stood the twenty men.

The major ordered the platoon to take aim.

"Aim," said the second lieutenant.

The platoon raised their rifles to their shoulders.

"Order them to fire," the major shouted.

"Fire," said the second lieutenant.

The platoon carried out the order. But they fired high. The rifle bullets went so high above their heads that the condemned men, impassive, made scarcely a movement.

Had there been any concerted plan of action between the firing squad and those whom they were ordered to execute, the latter could have dropped to the ground, feigning death. But nothing had passed between them except a few glances. After the volley one of the twenty smiled. The major lost his temper altogether. Revolver in hand, he went towards the condemned men, his face contorted with rage. He stopped in front of them and cried out:

"Very well, I shall punish the mutineers myself!"

He had time to fire three shots. The first struck

one of the men in the head so that he fell heavily to the ground; the second and the third brought down two others, both of whom were hit in the chest.

Captain Fiorelli drew his revolver, and shouted: "You're mad, sir!"

The firing squad, acting without orders, turned their weapons on the major and fired. He fell, riddled with bullets.

It was now only a few minutes to zero hour. The naval ordnance of 149 and 152 mm. had lengthened their range and were no longer firing on us. Our trenches, however, had been destroyed, and of the covering parties left there, only a few men were still alive. But in the enemy trenches and wire, huge breaches had been opened to the assaulting troops. My own battalion was massed in the trenches. I saw the 5th and 6th companies, followed by the 7th and 8th, leaving them *en masse* and reaching the enemy front line. We followed immediately afterwards, but attacked farther to the right. The 1st battalion and a battalion belonging to another regiment in the bri-·gade also occupied the enemy positions, which were full of dead.

These four battalions were the only ones between Val d'Assa and Cima Caldiera who attained their objective. On the rest of the front the attack failed. The mine at point 1496 on the extreme left of our division burst on our own men, making the enemy positions inaccessible. Our losses were very great. I started out that day as a company commander, and finished up in command of two battalions, the 3rd and the 1st, both of which had lost their commanding officers.

As the attack had succeeded in our sector alone, our advanced positions, which were open to enfilading fire by the enemy, became untenable. When night fell, we received orders to fall back on the line from which we had started. That night Captain Fiorelli came to see me, utterly exhausted. He told me about Major Melchiorri's death, for which he believed himself partly responsible. He said he had done his utmost to find death during the attack; but fate had decided to spare him. He therefore considered it his duty to report the whole matter to regimental headquarters. I did not succeed in dissuading him. The following day he put in a written report, inculpating himself. The brigade, division, and army corps headquarters were immediately informed of it. Together with the adjutant of the 2nd battalion and the second lieutenant of the 6th company, he was put under arrest and handed over to the military tribunal. On their way down the line the three officers, accompanied by a captain of carabineers and an escort, passed through my battalion. As they did so, the men all stood at attention and saluted them.

Chapter 29

I CAN ONLY SET DOWN OR RECALL THOSE THINGS THAT made the deepest impression on me. The attack was repeated on the 19th of June, but my battalion, which had lost most heavily, was left as brigade reserve and took no part in the action.

The wounded belonging to the battalion had, for the most part, been taken to the rear by divisional ambulances and evacuated to hospitals in the back area. Avellini, who was one of the most serious cases, had been left at the camp hospital, near Croce di Sant' Antonio. He had been wounded while in the enemy trench, at the head of his company, and his wounds were so grave that he could not be moved. He had lost an eye, but his worst injury was an abdominal one. Before being taken away by the stretcher-bearers he had asked to speak to me, and I had realized at the first glance that he was in a very bad way. He had had to make a great effort to raise himself on the stretcher and had fallen back in a faint. I had not seen him again since then. Although the battalion was in reserve behind the line, service duties prevented me from going to visit him; but I was able to telephone to the medical officer in charge of the hospital and get news of him now and then. His temperature remained high.

On the 22nd the medical officer in charge telephoned to say that Avellini wanted to see me at once, and that there was no time to lose, because his condition was hopeless. I asked the regimental commander for a few hours' leave, which was granted me.

How changed I found my friend! He had eaten nothing since the 10th, because owing to his abdominal wound he was unable to take any food. Of old so strong and full of life, he was now utterly exhausted. Stretched on a camp bed, motionless and with bloodless lips, he looked like a corpse. Only a movement of his mouth, like a bitter smile, showed that he still lived and suffered. I felt at once that this was the end; and I thought of his dreams of a military career, of service on the General Staff, of promotion, of the great national army. . . . Poor Avellini!

He had bandages over both his eyes, so that he could not see me when I came in. But he heard my footsteps and guessed at once who it was. He spoke my name, but in a voice so weak that I could scarcely hear it.

"Yes," I replied. "It's me. Don't speak. You mustn't tire yourself. I'll do all the talking. The surgeon told me that you've a good chance of recovery; but you mustn't fatigue yourself. The whole battalion's thinking of you and hoping to see you again soon. You must keep your mind on getting better. There's no hurry. The war will last all right. Everyone sends you messages, especially the men of your company."

"The men?"

"Yes. I specially went to see them before coming on here. The colonel wanted to be remembered to you too, and I've got good news for you from him."

"Thank you. Let's talk a little. But I'm done for, you know!"

"Don't talk nonsense. You've got to think of getting better."

The least effort caused him intense suffering. Even the few words he had spoken had tired him. His whole face was convulsed with pain. I had some news for him that would surely give him pleasure. Perhaps he would cheer up a little.

"I've splendid news for you. Guess what it is!"

He made a gesture with his hand. Was it curiosity or indifference? I went on.

"You have been recommended for the silver medal for distinguished valour on the field of battle. And also for promotion to captain for your war service. Brigade headquarters have already concurred; so it's quite certain that both recommendations will go through. That's what the colonel wanted me to tell you."

He raised his emaciated hand and let it fall again

with an expression of helplessness. It seemed as if he were saying: What's the good of all that?

"I asked you to come," he said, "because— Stay with me for a while. I want to tell you something." He spoke with great difficulty.

"You remember that packet of letters?"

"Yes, of course."

"In my case, which is with the baggage, you'll find there are two. Two packets. You know whom to send them to."

I forced myself to take this lightly, in order to cheer him a little, so I said:

"But those letters bring luck. They did in the matter of the mine. Now that you're wounded, they will again."

"Oh, yes. They bring luck all right. You can send them, but I'd rather you took them yourself; and I want this one to go with them."

I had not realized that beneath his outstretched hand a letter was lying on the bed. He took it up and showed it to me.

"Please read it to me. But come close, quite close."

I took the letter and sat down as near to him as I could. The envelope was unopened.

"Do you want me to open it?" I asked.

"Yes. But come closer still!"

I leaned over the bed, looking at the envelope as I did so. It was addressed to him, and the postmark was that of Marostica. My hand was trembling, but I opened it and took out two sheets of paper. I had not the courage to read them.

"Have you opened it?" he asked.

"Yes."

"Then read it to me, will you please?"

I unfolded the sheets, and my gaze hurried to the signature. It was that of the fair-haired girl we knew. I started reading the letter to him, in a voice that trembled.

"My darling . . ."

Avellini put his hands to his bandaged eyes, almost as if he wished to hide his tears from me. He was weeping. I stopped reading and did not speak. I let him weep without saying a word. A few minutes later he said:

"Go on, will you?"

I went on. No woman could have written more tender words than those I read that day. I had to stop reading more than once, for Avellini could not control his grief.

"What does dying matter to me?"

I finished the letter. He begged me to read it to him again; and I did so, often breaking off, as before, so deeply moved was he.

Then he took the letter in his hands and put it slowly to his lips.

"Let me keep it," he said. "Come and get it after my death."

My leave was up, and it was time for me to go back to the battalion. I no longer dared to talk to him of recovery. Standing up, I said to him:

"Is there anything I can tell your men? Or the colonel?"

"Yes, please. Thank him."

Then he pulled me towards him and whispered:

"Go to her. I want you to go to her yourself. I want you to tell her that my last thoughts were of her. That I've been thinking of no one else but her. And that I died happy."

I hurried back to the battalion. But I was so upset that when I reached it I went on walking till I came to the front line. Only then did I realize that I had overshot my battalion position by nearly a mile.

I had no sooner returned to battalion headquarters than I was called to the telephone. It was the medical officer at the hospital. In a roundabout way he began to tell me that Avellini was worse, that there was no more hope. At last he said outright that he was dead and that he had left a letter for me.

I left the hut that served as headquarters. Officers and orderlies were standing about, near, but I did not know what to say or what to do. Then I started off towards the 9th company. I felt compelled to bring them the sad tidings myself. The only officer who had survived the action on the 10th was a second lieutenant who had now taken command. He had been very much attached to Avellini. I was unable to beat about the bush with him, and said quite simply:

"Avellini's dead. He died a few minutes ago."

"Avellini's dead?" asked the second lieutenant.

"Yes, dead," I replied.

He looked at me in astonishment.

"Dead," he repeated. "Dead!"

It seemed to me as if some confusing thoughts which had nothing to do with us, or with the news that he had heard, had crossed his mind—merely for an instant. He quickly put out his hand for a bottle of brandy which was by his side, poured out a wine-glassful, and drank it at a gulp as if it had been medicine.

"What!" I said to him angrily. "I bring you news that your company commander's dead and you start drinking in the presence of your commanding officer. Do you think that's the way to behave?"

The second lieutenant seemed to wake as from a dream. He grew confused.

"Excuse me, sir," he said. "I did it without thinking, involuntarily. I realize it now. Please excuse me, sir."

I retraced my steps to headquarters. Life seemed unbearably sad to me. Now Avellini had gone too. Of my former fellow-officers in the battalion not one remained. Ottolenghi had been badly wounded on the 10th, and I had no idea to what hospital he had been taken. Once more I found myself alone. Once more they had all gone. And now I should have to look for the letters, recount everything, explain everything. It is not true that the instinct of self-preservation is always uppermost in life. There are moments when life is a greater burden than the thought of death.

Chapter 30

IN THE MIDDLE OF JULY THE BRIGADE WAS WITHDRAWN for a rest. My battalion encamped between Asiago and Gallio, on the reserve line along Monte Sisemol, to carry out defensive works. We were still within range of enemy artillery fire, but well sheltered in narrow valleys. Occasionally a single enemy reconnaissance machine flew over us at a great height and was quickly chased away by our fighting squadrons from the base at Bassano. Bombing planes never disturbed our rest. So it was that the tragic days through which we had just passed were followed by others almost happy. Men who had been lightly wounded rejoined the battalion, and new arrivals, both officers and men, came to fill the gaps that had been made in the ranks. Grisoni, the cavalry lieutenant, after a long convalescence was again posted to the battalion and took over command of the 12th company. He was still limping as a result of the wound he had received at Monte Fior, but had not lost his good spirits, and his gaiety greatly helped to dissipate our gloom. One

very soon began to forget. Life regained its ascend-
ancy. My orderly, who had also been wounded, rejoined from hospital. He once more took up his study
of the book on birds and I that of Baudelaire and
Ariosto.

One day, towards sunset, I was on the main road
leading from the Valle di Ronchi to Monte Sisemol.
I was returning from regimental headquarters, which
had been moved to Ronchi. On the way I met a colonel alone, mounted on a chestnut horse. I too was on
horseback and alone. Saluting the colonel, I continued on my way, but I had gone only a few paces
when I heard my name called. I looked round and
saw that the colonel wanted to speak to me, so I turned
my horse and rode back to him.

"Yes, sir?" I said.

"Come here. Have you forgotten your old commanding officer?"

It was Colonel Abbati. The reader may remember
the lieutenant-colonel whom I met with at Stoccaredo
and also at Monte Fior. It was he. The red braiding
beneath his badges of rank showed that he was now in
command of a regiment.

"You must forgive me, sir. I didn't recognize you."

It was indeed hard to recognize him at first sight.
He was much thinner and seemed greatly aged. His
previous liverish pallor had turned to lemon yellow
and his eyes were sunk in their sockets. He seemed
tired and ill.

Having asked me some questions about my regiment, he then said:

"Have you started drinking yet?"

"No, sir, I've gone on as before."

"I no longer know whether it's a good thing or not. The question's not so simple as I thought. Do you think I've changed?"

"You look tired, sir. Rather tired, but not really much changed."

"Rather tired? I'm finished. They'll make me a general soon—for my long service to the brandy flask. Colonel Abbati has succeeded in killing the troubles of war, but brandy has killed Colonel Abbati."

"What in the world do you mean, sir?"

"The war has ceased to be a contest between infantry and infantry, or artillery and artillery. It is a war of canteen against canteen, cask against cask, bottle against bottle. As far as I'm concerned, the Austrians have won. I admit that I'm defeated. Look at me: I'm done for. Don't you think I look like a defeated man?"

"I think you look very well on horseback, sir."

"I ought to have drunk water, and plenty of coffee. But now it's too late. Coffee is a stimulant but does not burn one up as spirits do. I've burnt up my brain; there's nothing in my head now but spent embers. I go on raking them, raking them, in the hope of finding some fragment that isn't burnt out, but there's not one left. I only wish we still had ice and snow; but now even the cold's gone, and in this damned heat I can see nothing but guns and rifles, dead bodies and groaning wounded men. I look for shade as if it were salvation. But it won't be for long. Well, good day!"

A few days later, about noon, I was at mess with the officers of the battalion. We were waiting for a second lieutenant of the 11th company, whom I had sent to regimental headquarters to draw some stores. It was time for mess, but the second lieutenant had still not arrived, so we sat down at table without him. He came in when we had almost finished eating.

"You're half an hour late," some of the younger officers called out. "You're fined two bottles."

"Has he got to pay?" asked the officer in charge of the mess.

"Yes," everyone shouted in chorus.

"All right. Two bottles it is! But I must tell you why I'm late."

"That doesn't matter," the cavalry lieutenant said. "We'll be content with the two bottles."

"No, I want to tell you what happened."

Everyone sitting at the table was now listening.

"I was coming from Ronchi along the road that runs alongside the mountain torrent. The sun was very hot. When I'd got as far up as the white house, where the trees shade the whole road thickly, I saw a man on horseback, riding slowly along and trying to. keep out of the sun. When he reached the trees, the horse stopped, in the shade. He then scrambled up on the saddle, climbed on to a branch, and disappeared among the leaves. All I could see was the horse, which did not move. I stayed where I was, hidden from view. A few minutes later the man reappeared among the branches, head downwards, hanging from his legs. I was astonished. I thought it must be someone doing gymnastics, although it seemed odd to me that anyone should do them like that. I still did not show myself, and neither the man nor the horse noticed that there was anyone near. The man let himself fall on to the saddle, supporting himself on his hands, and then reassumed a normal position on his mount. He rested a moment, then took out a flask and had a drink. Then he put away the flask and started the exercise all over again. He climbed into the branches and disappeared, only to reappear soon afterwards head downwards. He got back into the saddle and had another drink. I stayed where I was for about half an hour. The road was deserted. He repeated the whole operation three times. I wanted to get nearer in order to see more, but a cart came along at a trot, which caused the man to put spurs to his horse and disappear."

"Was the horse a chestnut?" I asked.

"Yes."

"With two white stockings?"

"Yes, with two white stockings."

"Didn't you notice whether the rider was an officer?"

"I couldn't see, because I was some way off, in the sun, while he was in deep shade, where it was almost dark."

"Was he short and thin?"

"Yes, he looked very short and thin to me."

There was no doubt about it. It was poor Colonel Abbati. He was evidently nearing his end.

Over the coffee the conversation grew animated. A second lieutenant who was an arts student at the University of Rome recited a satire of Juvenal's in Latin, following it up with his own version in Italian verse.

"As far as I'm concerned," Lieutenant Grisoni said, "you could have spared me the Latin. I studied it for ten years, and I was always at the top of the class, yet I didn't understand a word of what you said. Partly, perhaps, because you pronounce Latin as if you'd got a potato in your mouth."

Everyone was in high spirits. We might have been far out of range of the enemy's guns. We breathed freely once again, and the war seemed over and forgotten.

The ringing of a telephone bell interrupted our conversation. I got up and took the receiver, while the officers stopped their talk. It was the adjutant of the 1st battalion, who wanted to speak to me from regimental headquarters.

"What is it?" I asked.

"I wanted to warn you," he said, "that the regiment's moving tomorrow."

"Down to the plain, for a real rest?" I asked cheerfully.

"No, there's going to be no rest for us."

"Oh, where are we going?"

"To the Bainsizza plateau. An offensive has been started on that front and the army commander has personally asked for our brigade."

"What an honour!"

"Is your battalion ready?"

"Yes, the battalion is ready. But is it certain that we're to be sent to the Bainsizza?"

"Quite certain. I decoded the order myself."

"At what time do we start?"

"You'll be told tomorrow, when the battalion commanders report."

"Very well. Good-bye."

"Good-bye."

The officers held their breath. They had not been able to hear the adjutant's words, but from my replies they had understood only too well. They looked at me silently, in anxious suspense. Then the cavalry lieutenant filled up his glass and said:

"Here's to the Bainsizza!"

His fellow-officers did the same.

"To the offensive on the Bainsizza!"

It was beginning all over again.